GEOMETRY:
Modern Mathematics
via the
Euclidean Plane

LAWRENCE S. LEVY
University of Wisconsin

Prindle, Weber & Schmidt, Inc.
Boston, Massachusetts

The high contrast cover photo of a portion of Boston City Hall is adapted with permission from "Crafts 1970" publicity graphics, which were designed by Marcia McGinnis Shortt and sponsored by the Institute of Contemporary Art, with the assistance of the Boston Redevelopment Authority.

Overview

Since the Euclidean Plane contains all the ingredients of abstract algebra as well as the real and complex number systems, it provides an ideal opportunity to introduce students to modern mathematics "by encounter" rather than "by definition."

This book was written to present this view—in a one-semester or two-quarter course—to an audience which has the mathematical maturity, the knowledge of plane geometry, and the intuitive acquaintance with limits commonly provided by three semesters of analytic geometry and calculus at the college level. (Although a limit is taken in a few places in this presentation, calculus itself is not used.)

While working on the problem of classifying all isometries of the plane —a problem whose answer is by no means obvious—the student sees how the non-commutative arithmetic of function-composition can provide insight into a purely geometric problem. The Classification Theorem for Isometries is applied to the study of symmetries of polygons, and this leads naturally to the study of groups of isometries (but the definition of an abstract group is deliberately avoided). The first chapter ends with the proof (partly given in the form of problems) that every finite group of isometries of the plane is the group of *all* symmetries of some polygon. This is, in turn, applied to deduce the purely geometric fact that every polygon with at least two symmetries different from the identity must have a center of symmetry.

Chapter 2 presents the basic geometric facts about the complex numbers at the high-school level for those students who have not seen them previously. The chapter also gives the other students a chance to acquaint themselves with terminology and notation which will appear later in this book.

Chapter 3 uses the complex numbers to classify all similarities of the plane. The final section proves (partly in the form of problems) the theorem that any one-to-one function of the plane into itself which preserves circles and lines must be a similarity, thus giving a precise meaning to the metatheorem that similarities are precisely those one-to-one functions from the plane into itself which preserve the shapes of geometric figures.

Chapter 4, "Circular Inversion," completes the main section of this book. Inversion was chosen as the final "transformation" topic because it combines the modern spirit of the preceding material on geometric functions with a powerful tool for proving old-fashioned theorems about the geometry of circles. The basic theorems (about changing circles to lines, reversing angles, etc.) are proved by means of the complex numbers; and the chapter ends with a discussion of the inversive plane which ties inversion together with similarity and isometry and, as an application, analyzes the linear fractional transformation.

Chapters 5, 6, and 7 contain supplementary topics: a geometric proof of the Fundamental Theorem of Algebra (Chapter 6); a proof that, given two polygons of equal area, the first can be dissected into a finite number of sub-polygons which can be reassembled to form the second (Chapter 5); and a discussion of Pythagorean triples (Chapter 7).

The Prependix, which appears at the beginning of the book, consists of an informal discussion of the meaning of "mathematical proof." It, together with Chapters 1 through 4, should provide enough material for a tightly organized one-semester course. The author hopes this book will contribute to the solution of that most difficult of all pedagogical problems in college mathematics: **to bridge the** *mathematical maturity gap* **between elementary calculus and advanced undergraduate courses** such as abstract algebra and real variables.

The author suggests the following scheme to a teacher for classroom use of the book. *One-semester course:* The first time, go as far as possible through the Prependix and first four chapters. For variety from semester to semester, a teacher can replace the last sections of Chapters 1, 3, and 4 by selections from Chapters 5, 6, and 7 without disturbing the continuity of the text. *Two-quarter course:* Do the entire book.

Lawrence S. Levy
University of Wisconsin

Contents

Prependix.
Mathematical
Proof

Before beginning the mainstream of this book we examine, briefly, the principal ingredients of a mathematical proof.

Consider, first, the problem of computing the sum $S = 1 + 2 + 3 + \cdots + 100$. One solution would be to actually "add up" these numbers—an uninspiring task, to say the least. Another difficulty here involves accuracy. Suppose two people, after performing the addition, get answers of 5124 and 4998. Who is right? Probably neither. (At least, the author doesn't know anyone who can add 100 numbers without making at least one error!)

Another approach to a solution is to write down the sum twice, once forward and once backward, and then to add columns as shown below.

$$
\begin{array}{llll}
S = & 1 + & 2 + & 3 + \cdots + & 99 + 100 \\
S = & 100 + & 99 + & 98 + \cdots + & 2 + 1 \\
\hline
2S = & \overline{101} + & \overline{101} + & \overline{101} + \cdots + & \overline{101} + \overline{101} \quad \text{(100 sums on the right)}
\end{array}
$$

It is then clear that $2S = (100) \cdot (101)$, so that $S = (50) \cdot (101) = 5050$.

Thus we see the most important ingredient of a mathematical proof—the use of "logical reasoning", in place of the brute force of direct computation or measurement, in order to uncover some principle which makes an accurate answer easier to obtain and check.

Consider, next, the theorem from elementary plane geometry: *An angle inscribed in arc of a circle has half the number of degrees as the arc it intercepts.* (See Figures P.1, P.2, and P.3. Note that there are two arcs AC in each diagram. The one containing point B is the one in which angle β is *inscribed*; the one not containing B is the arc which β intercepts.)

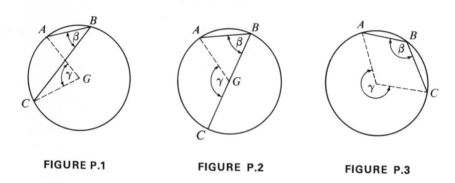

FIGURE P.1   **FIGURE P.2**   **FIGURE P.3**

Since the central angle γ at G has the same number of degrees as the intercepted arc AC in question, the theorem states that $\gamma = 2\beta$.

Direct computation and measurement are even less helpful in checking the correctness of this theorem than in the preceding problem, since it is not possible to measure *all* possible angles β and γ, and since the accuracy of any measurements which are made is limited to the accuracy of the measuring equipment used.

Here is one of the conventional proofs of this theorem. Consider first the case that line segment BC contains the center G of the given circle (Figure P.2). Then triangle AGB is isosceles because its sides AG and BG are radii of the same circle. Therefore its angles at A and B are equal. The exterior angle γ of this triangle at G is equal to the sum of the two opposite interior angles; that is, $\gamma = \beta + \beta$ as desired. (*Alternative.* Since the sum of the angles of a triangle is 180°, angle G of triangle ABG has $180 - (\text{angle } A) - (\text{angle } B) = 180 - \beta - \beta = 180 - 2\beta$ degrees. Hence $\gamma = 180° - (\text{angle } G \text{ of triangle } ABG) = 180 - (180 - 2\beta) = 2\beta$.)

Exercise 1. Prove the theorem for the cases shown in Figures P.1 and P.3. (*Hint.* Draw the diameter containing *BG* and reduce to the case considered in the text.)

The above proof will be convincing only to those who "know" that base angles of an isosceles triangle are equal, as well as one of the two theorems concerning sums of angles of triangles. These theorems can be proved by using simpler theorems which, in turn, can be proved by using still simpler theorems. Eventually we must work our way back, in this chain of "simpler" theorems, to an assertion which we do not prove.

Thus, in order to make a mathematical proof really complete it is necessary to have (i) a list of statements (called *axioms*) which all will accept as correct without proof, and (ii) a list of the acceptable rules of logical reasoning. The proof of a theorem would then be complete only when it had been reduced by the rules of reasoning (ii) to one or more of the axioms (i) or to one or more theorems proved by (ii) from (i).

It is possible to write a complete list of axioms for the Euclidean plane, but such a list is very long and complicated. In fact the learning of this list, together with a thorough discussion of the allowable rules of reasoning and the meaning of "line", "point", "length", etc., would take up an entire course if we wanted to get as far as the "side-angle-side" theorems for congruence and similarity of triangles. To see why this is the case, consider what axioms would be necessary to prove the following two very simple theorems.

(1) *Two distinct circles cannot meet more than twice.*

(2) *Let* λ *be a line,* α *a circle. If a moving point P traces* α *in the counterclockwise direction, then the reflection P′ of P in* λ *traces the reflection* α′ *of* α *in the clockwise direction* (Figures P.4. and P.5).

In order to proceed with the rest of this book without first spending an entire course on fundamentals, we will compromise with the ideal proof described above and accept theorems such as (1) and (2) as "obvious". In addition, theorems ordinarily included in basic Euclidean plane geometry courses (such as: The sum of the angles of a triangle equals 180°) will be considered already proved, although individual readers may occasionally need to supply additional details because *their* courses in basic plane geometry did not cover exactly the same theorems as did the author's.

In conclusion, the most important criterion a mathematical proof must

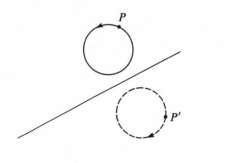

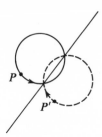

FIGURE P.4   **FIGURE P.5**

satisfy is this: *Is the truth of the theorem clearer to the reader after he has read and understood the proof than it was before that?*

Exercise 2. Prove that the angle β between two intersecting chords of a circle has half the number of degrees as the sum of the two arcs which the angle intercepts (Figure P.6). (*Hint.* Draw line segment *CE*.)

Exercise 3. Prove that the angle between a tangent ray (ray $\overrightarrow{BT}$ in Figure P.7) and a chord of a circle drawn to the point of tangency has half the number of degrees as the arc the angle intercepts. (*Remark.* This follows immediately by taking a limit, in Figure P.1, P.2, or P.3, as ray $\overrightarrow{BA}$ approaches tangency. Give a proof which uses more "Euclidean" rules of reasoning by drawing line *BG* in Figure P.7, *G* the center of the circle.)

Exercise 4. Prove that, in Figure P.6, $(CB)\cdot(BD)=(AB)\cdot(BE)$. (*Hint.* Draw *AC* and *ED* and look for similar triangles.)

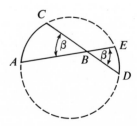

FIGURE P.6

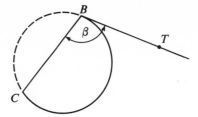

FIGURE P.7

Problem. State and prove the version of Exercise 2 for which point *B* is outside the circle. Then take a limit to get a theorem in which both of the line segments are tangent to the circle.

TRANSFORMATIONS

Isometries in the Plane

1.1   INTRODUCTION

The two basic relations one studies in Euclidean geometry are congruence and similarity (of triangles, polygons, and circles). The assertion that triangle a is congruent to triangle b means that there is a *rigid motion* of triangle a which carries it to triangle b. The word "rigid" refers to the fact that triangle a does not change shape as it is moved. For example, in Figure 1.1, triangle a can be carried to triangle b by moving it the distance CC' to the right, and then rotating the resulting triangle $90°$ counterclockwise about C'.

Note that we have described two rigid motions of the entire plane—translation through the distance CC' to the right, followed by a rotation about C'.

The main problem of this chapter will be: *Describe all rigid motions of*

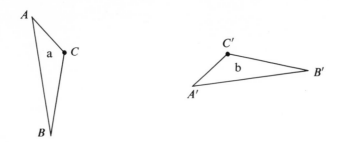

FIGURE 1.1

the plane. Before we can solve this problem it will be necessary to establish some terminology which will enable us to discuss it more precisely. An example of an ambiguity which presently exists is the question of whether we will consider a 90° counterclockwise rotation of the plane about C' to be "the same" rigid motion as a 270° clockwise rotation about C'. These are certainly different motions; but if a point P is carried to a point Q by the 90° counterclockwise rotation, then it will also be carried to the same point Q by the 270° clockwise rotation. Since we are studying rigid motions as the method of achieving a congruence, *we will want to consider two motions "the same" if they have the same effect upon every point of the plane*. We will take care of this semantic difficulty by replacing the physical notion of a motion with the mathematical notion of a point-valued function which will be called an *isometry*.

Point-valued functions are introduced in Section 1.2; and isometries in Section 1.3. The task of describing all isometries of the plane is carried out in Section 1.4. Finally, in Sections 1.5 and 1.6 the theory of isometries is used to find some interesting properties of symmetry.

1.2   POINT FUNCTIONS

Let $\mathcal{A}$ and $\mathcal{B}$ be sets of points in the plane. We wish to define a function f from $\mathcal{A}$ to $\mathcal{B}$ (*Notation.* $f: \mathcal{A} \to \mathcal{B}$). From each point P of $\mathcal{A}$ imagine an arrow drawn to a point—which we will call P^f—of $\mathcal{B}$ (see Figure 1.2). We do not assume here that every point of $\mathcal{B}$ is actually "hit" by the head of an arrow; nor that the heads of distinct arrows hit distinct points of $\mathcal{B}$. (For instance, the arrows beginning at Q and R both hit the same point of $\mathcal{B}$.)

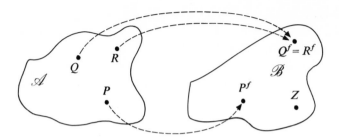

FIGURE 1.2

In somewhat more precise language, we say that a *function f from* $\mathscr{A}$ *to* $\mathscr{B}$ is a collection of pairings, $P \to P^f$, exactly one for each point P of $\mathscr{A}$ to a point P^f of $\mathscr{B}$. For example, let $\mathscr{A}$ be the square consisting of all points (x, y) in the plane such that $0 \le x \le 2$ and $0 \le y \le 2$ (see Figure 1.3), and let $\mathscr{B}$ be a line segment 5 units long. Then, for a point $P = (x, y)$ in $\mathscr{A}$ let P^f be the point of $\mathscr{B}$ whose distance from the left-hand endpoint of $\mathscr{B}$ is $x + y$. Thus $(0, 0)^f$ is the left-hand endpoint of $\mathscr{B}$; and if $P = (1, 1\frac{1}{2})$, then P^f is the midpoint of $\mathscr{B}$.

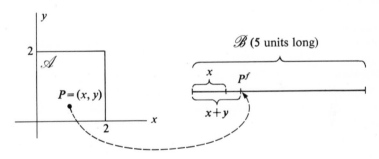

FIGURE 1.3

Problem 1. Find all points $P = (x, y)$ such that P^f is the midpoint of $\mathscr{B}$, f the function described above. (*Hint.* The answer will be a line segment.)

Note that while P^f is a *point* of $\mathscr{B}$, the *function f* is the collection of pairings P to P^f, and *not* a collection of points.

For a second example of a point function, choose $\mathscr{A}$ and $\mathscr{B}$ each to be the whole plane, and for each point P of the plane let P^g be the point which can be reached by moving P one inch east, then one inch north. It is often convenient to think of a function g (as in this example) as the motion which takes every point P to P^g. This can be helpful, but can also be slightly misleading. To see why, let P^{g_1} be the point which can be reached by moving P northeast $\sqrt{2}$ inches. This is illustrated by the dotted arrow in Figure 1.4.

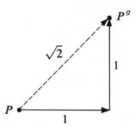

FIGURE 1.4

Note that although we have used two different *motions* to define g and g_1, the two collections of *pairings* $P \to P^g$ and $P \to P^{g_1}$ are the same because $P^g = P^{g_1}$ for every point P in the plane. Thus g and g_1 are the *same function*, although they have been described in terms of two different motions.

Problem 2*.† Let A and B be points in the plane with B one inch east of A. For each point P in the plane let P^h be the point which can be reached by rotating P 90° *counter*clockwise about A and then rotating the resulting point P' 90° *clock*wise about B (see Figure 1.5). Is the function h the same as or different from the functions g and g_1 described above? [A correct solution will consist of either proving that $P^h = P^{g_1}$ for every point P in the plane, or else locating a point P such that $P^h \neq P^{g_1}$.] (*Hint.* Try analytic geometry.)

Now return to an arbitrary function $f: \mathscr{A} \to \mathscr{B}$, where $\mathscr{A}$ and $\mathscr{B}$ are sets of points in the plane (Figure 1.1). We will say that f is *onto* (*Notation.* $f: \mathscr{A}$ onto $\mathscr{B}$) if every point of $\mathscr{B}$ is hit by the head of some arrow—that is, if for each point Z in $\mathscr{B}$ there is at least one point P in $\mathscr{A}$ such that $P^f = Z$. We will say that f is *one-to-one* if whenever $P \neq Q$ (both being points of $\mathscr{A}$)

† An asterisk following a problem number indicates a more difficult problem.

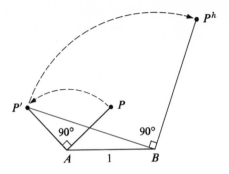

FIGURE 1.5

we must have $P^f \neq Q^f$—that is, if two distinct points of $\mathscr{A}$ never are sent by f to the same point of $\mathscr{B}$.

Note that the function g described above is both one-to-one and onto. However, the function f described in Figure 1.2 using addition of coordinates is neither one-to-one $[(\frac{1}{2}, 1)^f = (\frac{3}{4}, \frac{3}{4})^f]$ nor onto, since the distance of $(x, y)^f$ from the left endpoint of $\mathscr{B}$ is at most $2 + 2 = 4$ for any (x, y) in $\mathscr{A}$. Thus the right endpoint of $\mathscr{B}$ cannot have the form $(x, y)^f$, regardless of the choice of (x, y) in $\mathscr{A}$. Note, however, that if we let $\mathscr{C}$ be the left-most four inches of $\mathscr{B}$, then f, considered as a function from $\mathscr{A}$ to $\mathscr{C}$, becomes onto.

Problem 3. Let $\mathscr{P}$ be the portion of the parabola $y = x^2/2$ which lies in the square $\mathscr{A}$—that is, such that $0 \leq x \leq 2$—and consider the function given by $(x, y)^f = x + y$ to be a function from $\mathscr{P}$ to the line segment $\mathscr{C}$ defined above. Is this new smaller function f one-to-one? Is it onto?

Problem 4. Let 0 and A be given points such that the ray $\overrightarrow{0A}$ (that is, line segment $0A$ together with its extension through A) is horizontal and points eastward. Given an angle θ (measured counterclockwise) and a positive number r, we can locate the point P as in Figure 1.6 (by its *polar coordinates* $[r, \theta]$).

(a) Letting $\mathscr{B}$ be the plane with 0 removed, define a function $k : \mathscr{B} \to \mathscr{B}$ by $[r, \theta]^k = [2r, 2\theta]$ where $0 \leq \theta < 360°$. Is k one-to-one? onto?

(b) Using the same $\mathscr{B}$, define $k_1 : \mathscr{B} \to \mathscr{B}$ by $[r, \theta]^{k_1} = [r/2, \theta/2]$ where $0 \leq \theta < 360°$. Is k_1 one-to-one? onto?

An important operation can sometimes be performed on functions. It

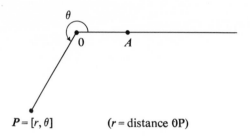

$P = [r, \theta]$ $\qquad$ $(r = \text{distance } 0P)$

FIGURE 1.6

is called *composition* and can be defined as follows. Let $f : \mathscr{A} \to \mathscr{B}$ and $g : \mathscr{B} \to \mathscr{C}$ be functions, where $\mathscr{A}$, $\mathscr{B}$, and $\mathscr{C}$ are subsets of the plane (see Figure 1.7). Then for any point P of $\mathscr{A}$, $Q = P^f$ is a point of $\mathscr{B}$ and hence Q^g is a point of $\mathscr{C}$. We call this last point $P^{f \circ g}$ (the result of applying f, then g to P) and call the resulting function $f \circ g : \mathscr{A} \to \mathscr{C}$ the *composition f then g*.

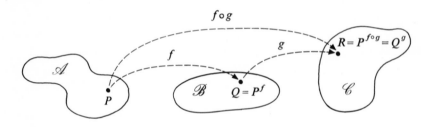

FIGURE 1.7

Caution. We have used a notation for composition, $f \circ g$, which resembles the notation for a product. However, it can happen that $g \circ f \ne f \circ g$. This can happen in an extreme way. For instance, if $\mathscr{C}$ has no points in common with $\mathscr{A}$, then there will be no points P for which both of the expressions $P^{f \circ g}$ and $P^{g \circ f}$ make sense. However, even when $\mathscr{A} = \mathscr{B} = \mathscr{C}$, so that this difficulty cannot arise, it can happen that $g \circ f \ne f \circ g$ for appropriately chosen f and g (see Problem 5).

However, whenever f, g, and h are functions such that (at least) one of the expressions $(f \circ g) \circ h$ and $f \circ (g \circ h)$ is meaningful, a moment of thought will show that both are meaningful, in fact equal; for they are merely different ways of writing "f then g then h". We will use the simpler notation $f \circ g \circ h$ for this situation.

Problem 5. Let λ be a horizontal line in the plane and r : (the plane) $\rightarrow$ (the plane) the function defined by $P^r =$ the reflection of P in λ. Define two other point function by $P^e =$ the point 1 inch east of P and $P^s =$ the point one inch south of P (see Figure 1.8). Does $r \circ s = s \circ r$? Does $r \circ e = e \circ r$?

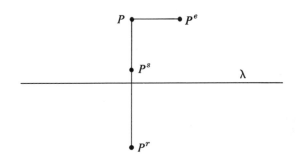

FIGURE 1.8

1.3   DEFINITION OF ISOMETRY. BASIC NOTATION

DEFINITION

An *isometry* of the plane is a one-to-one function : (the plane) onto (the plane), such that for all points P, Q of the plane

$$\text{dist}(P^f, Q^f) = \text{dist}(P, Q).$$

Here $\text{dist}(P, Q)$ is an abbreviation for "the distance from P to Q". The prefix "iso" means "the same" and "metric" means "measure" (as in "metric system", "psychometrics", "thermometer" or the dietary drink "Metrical"). In mathematics, "metric" is almost always used for a measure of distance.

We now list some of the most familiar isometries and the notation we will use for them. (The reader's attention is called to the fact that the index at the end of this book lists the pages on which technical terms and notation are defined.)

(i) *translation* [*Notation.* trans $\overrightarrow{AB}$]. Let a *directed line segment* $\overrightarrow{AB}$ (that is, a line segment on which A has been designated as the "beginning" and B as the "end") be given. We define $P^{\text{trans }\overrightarrow{AB}}$ to be the point reached by moving point P in the plane in the direction given by $\overrightarrow{AB}$ through the distance length (AB). Thus, if P is not on *line AB*, the figure $ABP^{\text{trans }\overrightarrow{AB}}P$ (see Figure 1.9) will be a parallelogram. The function trans $\overrightarrow{AB}$ will be called the *translation determined by the directed line segment* $\overrightarrow{AB}$.

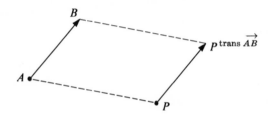

FIGURE 1.9

(ii) *rotation* [*Notation.* rot (A, θ)]. Here a point A and a directed angle θ are given. Then $P^{\text{rot}(A,\theta)}$ is defined to be the point reached by rotating P about A through the directed angle θ (see Figure 1.10). To remove possible ambiguity we define $A^{\text{rot}(A,\theta)}$ to be A itself. Note that, if $P \neq A$, triangle $PAP^{\text{rot}(A,\theta)}$ is isosceles.

We will follow the convention that rot $(A, 30°)$ means rotation about A

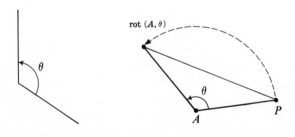

FIGURE 1.10

through 30° *counterclockwise.* When we want a 30° clockwise rotation we will write rot $(A, -30°)$ or rot $(A, 330°)$.

(iii) *reflection in a line* [*Notation.* refl λ]. Let λ be a given line. Then, for any point P not on λ draw the perpendicular PT from P to λ (Figure 1.11). $P^{\text{refl}\,\lambda}$ is then the point reached by extending line segment PT past T, a distance equal to length (PT). If P is on λ, then $P^{\text{refl}\,\lambda} = P$.

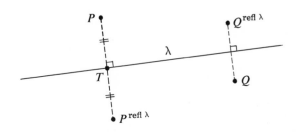

FIGURE 1.11

(iv) *reflection in a point* [no special notation]. Figure 1.12 shows the reflections P^r and Q^r of sample points P and Q in the point A.

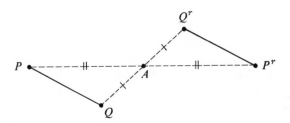

FIGURE 1.12

(v) The *identity function* [*Notation.* id]. Namely $P^{\text{id}} = P$ for every point P.

(vi) *Any composition of 2 or more of the above isometries.* For example, let A be a point on a line λ. Then rot $(A, 90°) \circ$ refl λ [that is, the function $P \rightarrow P^{\text{rot}(A,\,90°)\,\circ\,\text{refl}\,\lambda}$] is an isometry.

Exercise. Let A, B, and P be points located approximately as shown below. Figure 1.13 also shows the approximate location of the point $P^{\text{rot}(A,\,30°)\,\circ\,\text{trans}\,\vec{AB}}$.

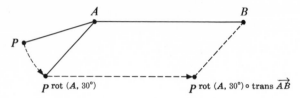

FIGURE 1.13

Locate (approximately) the points

(i) $P^{(\text{trans } \vec{AB}) \, \circ \, \text{rot}(A, 30)}$,   (ii) $A^{(\text{trans } \vec{AB}) \, \circ \, \text{rot}(A, 30°)}$,

(iii) $A^{\text{rot}(A, \, 30°) \, \circ \, \text{trans } \vec{AB}}$,   (iv) $B^{(\text{trans } \vec{AB}) \, \circ \, \text{rot}(A, 30°)}$,

(v) $B^{\text{rot}(A, \, 30°) \, \circ \, \text{trans } \vec{AB}}$.

Problem 1. Let A and B be distinct points (that is, $A \neq B$). Find all points P, if any, such that

$$P^{\text{rot}(A, \, 30°) \, \circ \, \text{trans } \vec{AB}} = P.$$

(Include a proof that your answer is correct.)

___

In giving the definition of isometry we singled out just one property of rigid motions, namely the preservation of distance. However, isometries preserve more than this. For example, *if f is an isometry and A, B, and C are collinear points, then so are A^f, B^f, and C^f* (Figure 1.14).

To see that this is true, note that $\text{dist}(A, B) + \text{dist}(B, C) = \text{dist}(A, C)$ since A, B and C are collinear. Hence, by the definition of "isometry",

(1) $\text{dist}(A^f, B^f) + \text{dist}(B^f, C^f) = \text{dist}(A^f, C^f).$

But for any point P *off* line segment $A^f C^f$ we must have

$$\text{dist}(A^f, P) + \text{dist}(P, C^f) > \text{dist}(A^f, C^f),$$

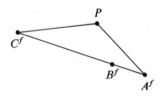

FIGURE 1.14

because the shortest distance between two points is the line segment joining them. Therefore (1) shows that B^f is *not off* line segment $A^f C^f$. In simpler language, B^f is *on* this segment. We have, in fact, proved more than was claimed, namely: *If A, B, and C are collinear with B between A and C, then A^f, B^f and C^f are collinear with B^f between A^f and C^f for every isometry f.*

Problem 2. Let A, B, C be non-collinear points. Show that, for every isometry f of the plane, angle $ABC =$ angle $A^f B^f C^f$.

Problem 3. Let A, B, C, and D be points which lie on a circle, and let f be any isometry of the plane. Show that A^f, B^f, C^f, and D^f all lie on a circle.

Problem 4. Show that, for all points P *above* a given horizontal line AB,

$$P^{\mathrm{rot}(A,\, 30°)\, \circ\, \mathrm{trans}\, \overrightarrow{AB}} = P^{\mathrm{trans}\, \overrightarrow{AB}\, \circ\, \mathrm{rot}(B,\, 30°)}$$

Problem 5. Let A, B be distinct points. Find all points P, if any, such that $P^{\mathrm{rot}(A,\, 30°)\, \circ\, \mathrm{trans}\, \overrightarrow{AB}} = P^{(\mathrm{trans}\, \overrightarrow{AB})\, \circ\, \mathrm{rot}(A,\, 30°)}$. (Include a proof that your answer is correct.) (*Hint.* Try coordinate geometry with $A = (0, 0)$ and $B = (0, 1)$.)

1.4   CLASSIFICATION OF ISOMETRIES

We now solve the problem central to this chapter: *Describe all isometries of the plane.* We shall want the answer expressed in a form which makes it easy to visualize all isometries *directly* (such as translations, reflections, ..., including whatever else may occur) rather than in the *abstract* terms of the defining property, $\mathrm{dist}(P, Q) = \mathrm{dist}(P^f, Q^f)$. The somewhat surprising answer will appear in Theorem 1.4.8. We approach the problem indirectly (as is the case with most difficult problems in mathematics), and require the following as our starting point:

DEFINITION

Let f be a function: (the plane) $\rightarrow$ (the plane). A *fixed point* of f is a point P such that $P^f = P$. For example, note that a rotation about a point has exactly one fixed point (namely, the center of the rotation) while a translation has no fixed points.

1.4.1   PROPOSITION

The set of fixed points of an isometry of the plane must be one of the following:

(i) The whole plane (in which case the isometry equals the identity function); or

(ii) A line (in which case the isometry must be reflection in that line); or

(iii) A single point; or

(iv) No points at all.

Our proof will require the following fact from elementary geometry.

1.4.2   LEMMA

If a point A is equally distant from two distinct points P and Q, then A lies on the perpendicular bisector of line segment PQ (see Figure 1.15).

Exercise. Prove the lemma.

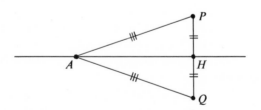

FIGURE 1.15

Proof of Proposition 1.4.1.   Let an isometry f of the plane be given. After listing the possibilities that f has no fixed points or exactly one fixed point, we may confine our attention to the case that f has at least two distinct fixed points A and B. Also, after listing the possibility that f is the identity function, we can suppose that f has at least one nonfixed point.

Let P be any point such that $P \neq P^f$. Where is P^f? By the definition of "isometry", $\operatorname{dist}(A, P) = \operatorname{dist}(A^f, P^f)$. Since $A = A^f$, this becomes $\operatorname{dist}(A, P) = \operatorname{dist}(A, P^f)$. Thus, by the lemma, A lies on the perpendicular bisector of line segment PP^f. By the same reasoning, B lies on this same perpendicular bisector; and, since exactly one straight line passes through two distinct points, we conclude that line AB is the perpendicular bisector of line segment PP^f. We can restate this in the form: *If $P \neq P^f$, then P^f is the reflection of P in line AB* (see Figure 1.16).

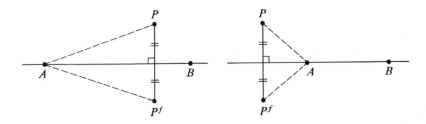

FIGURE 1.16

Finally, let Q be any point such that $Q = Q^f$. To locate such a Q, again choose any point P such that $P \neq P^f$. Since $Q = Q^f$ we get that $\operatorname{dist}(Q, P) = \operatorname{dist}(Q, P^f)$ so that, again by the lemma, Q lies on the perpendicular bisector AB of line segment PP^f. Thus Q is its own reflection in line AB.

We have now shown that for every point P, $P^f = P^{\operatorname{refl} AB}$. Therefore $f = \operatorname{refl} AB$. The proof of (ii), and hence of the entire proposition, is now complete. $\square$

1.4.3   REMARKS

Let g be a $1 - 1$ function: (the plane) onto (the plane). Then we can define the *inverse function* g^{-1}: (the plane) onto (the plane) by

$$X^{g^{-1}} = \text{that point } A \text{ such that } A^g = X.$$

Note that, since g is onto, there is at least one A such that $A^g = X$; and, since g is also $1 - 1$ there cannot be more than one such point A. Thus the definition makes sense. Note that $X^{g^{-1} \circ g} = A^g = X$ and $A^{g \circ g^{-1}} = X^{g^{-1}} = A$ for any choice of X. This also shows that $A^{g \circ g^{-1}} = A$ for every choice of A.

Hence
$$g^{-1} \circ g = \text{id} = g \circ g^{-1}$$

for every $1 - 1$ *function* g: (the plane) onto (the plane). This useful formula also explains the choice of notation g^{-1}.

Exercise. (a) Let f and g be $1 - 1$ functions: (the plane) onto (the plane). Establish the formula $(f \circ g)^{-1} = g^{-1} \circ f^{-1}$.
  (b) Find a pair of isometries f and g such that $(f \circ g)^{-1} \neq f^{-1} \circ g^{-1}$.

If g is an isometry of the plane, then so is g^{-1}. To see this, let $X^{g^{-1}} = A$ and $Y^{g^{-1}} = B$. Then
$$\text{dist}(X^{g^{-1}}, Y^{g^{-1}}) = \text{dist}(A, B) = \text{dist}(A^g, B^g) = \text{dist}(X, Y).$$
Another fact we will need is: *The composition of two isometries is again an isometry.*

Exercise. Give a proof.

These ideas will be used to prove:

1.4.4   COROLLARY

Let f and g be isometries of the plane which have the same effect on some three non-collinear points. Then $f = g$ (that is, $P^f = P^g$ for every point P).

Proof. Let A, B, and C be the three given non-collinear points such that $A^f = A^g$, $B^f = B^g$, and $C^f = C^g$. Then $A^{f \circ g^{-1}} = (A^f)^{g^{-1}} = A^{g \circ g^{-1}} = $ (by the definition of g^{-1} given in 1.4.3) A. Similarly, B and C are also fixed points of $f \circ g^{-1}$.

Since g^{-1} is an isometry and the composition of two isometries is again an isometry, we see that $f \circ g^{-1}$ is an isometry with three non-collinear fixed points. Therefore by Proposition 1.4.1, $f \circ g^{-1} = \text{id}$. (One of the possibilities enumerated in that proposition must hold; and it is clear that none of the last three hold. Hence the first does.) Composing on the right with g we see that
$$f \circ g^{-1} \circ g = (\text{id}) \circ g = g$$
and since $g^{-1} \circ g = \text{id}$ we get $f = g$ as desired.   ☐

Exercise. Using the above corollary, give a "2-line" solution of Problem 2*, Section 1.2.

1.4.5   COROLLARY

Let λ_1 and λ_2 be lines which meet at a point A. Then the composition $(\text{refl } \lambda_1) \circ (\text{refl } \lambda_2)$ equals the rotation $\text{rot}(A, 2\theta)$ where θ is the directed angle θ from λ_1 to λ_2 (Figure 1.17).

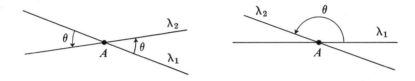

FIGURE 1.17

Proof. Choose a point P such that the directed angle φ from AP to λ_1 has the same sense (clockwise or counterclockwise) as θ but is less than θ. Then the points $Q = P^{\text{refl } \lambda_1}$ and $R = Q^{\text{refl } \lambda_2} = P^{(\text{refl } \lambda_1) \circ (\text{refl } \lambda_2)}$ are located as shown in Figure 1.18. Then right triangles APH and AQH are congruent by "side-angle-side" because they share side AH; they have equal (90°) angles at H; and $PH = QH$ (all by the definition of the reflection of P in λ_1). Hence the corresponding sides AP and AQ have the same length and $\sphericalangle HAQ$ also equals φ.

Similarly, length $AQ = $ length AR (hence length $AP = $ length AR), and

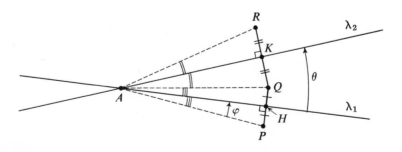

FIGURE 1.18

$\sphericalangle QAK = \sphericalangle KAR$. It follows that $\sphericalangle PAR$ equals twice $\sphericalangle HAK = \theta$. Therefore $R = P^{(\text{refl}\,\lambda_1)\,\circ\,\text{refl}\,\lambda_2}$ can be reached by rotating P about A through directed angle 2θ; that is, $P^{(\text{refl}\,\lambda_1)\,\circ\,\text{refl}\,\lambda_2} = P^{\text{rot}(A,\,2\theta)}$.

Since we can easily find three non-collinear points P such that the directed angle φ has the same sense as θ but is less than θ, we conclude from Corollary 1.4.4 that $(\text{refl}\,\lambda_1)\circ \text{refl}\,\lambda_2 = \text{rot}(A, 2\theta)$ as desired. $\square$

Note that the use of 1.4.4 has saved us painful separate consideration of many special cases, some of which have diagrams quite different from the one above. For example:

Problem 1. Draw a diagram showing the position of P, Q, and R when φ has the same sense as θ but is *greater* than θ. Then show (without using 1.4.5) that, for this P, $P^{(\text{refl}\,\lambda_1)\,\circ\,\text{refl}\,\lambda_2} = P^{\text{rot}(A,\,2\theta)}$.

1.4.6   COROLLARY

Let λ_1 and λ_2 be parallel lines. Then the composition $(\text{refl}\,\lambda_1)\circ(\text{refl}\,\lambda_2)$ equals translation through twice the directed distance from λ_1 to λ_2.

Problem 2. Give a proof of 1.4.6. (*Hint.* Model it after 1.4.5.) $\square$

The next theorem usually comes as a surprise to those who have not seen it previously. It shows that the preceding two corollaries are part of a more general phenomenon, sometimes known as "everything can be done by mirrors".

1.4.7   THEOREM

Every isometry of the plane can be expressed as the composition of two or three reflections in lines.

Proof. Let f be the given isometry. Our plan will be to compose f with reflections in order to obtain fixed points, and then apply 1.4.1.

Let A be any point and, if $A \neq A^f$, let λ be the perpendicular bisector of line segment AA^f (see Figure 1.19). Then $A^{f\,\circ\,\text{refl}\,\lambda} = A$. If $A = A^f$ let λ be *any* line containing A. We still have $A^{f\,\circ\,\text{refl}\,\lambda} = A$.

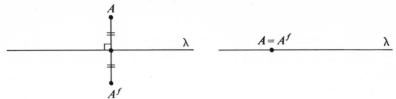

FIGURE 1.19

If $\mathrm{id} = f \circ \mathrm{refl}\,\lambda$ then we can compose both sides with $\mathrm{refl}\,\lambda$ (on the right), getting $\mathrm{refl}\,\lambda = f \circ (\mathrm{refl}\,\lambda) \circ (\mathrm{refl}\,\lambda) = f \circ \mathrm{id} = f$, since $(\mathrm{refl}\,\lambda) \circ (\mathrm{refl}\,\lambda) = \mathrm{id}$ for every line λ. Hence

$$f = \mathrm{refl}\,\lambda = (\mathrm{refl}\,\lambda) \circ (\mathrm{refl}\,\lambda) \circ (\mathrm{refl}\,\lambda),$$

a composition of three reflections, as claimed. (This, of course, is not the interesting part of the theorem.)

If $f \circ \mathrm{refl}\,\lambda \neq \mathrm{id}$ then $B^{f \circ \mathrm{refl}\,\lambda} \neq B$ for some B, and $B \neq A$ since A is fixed by $f \circ \mathrm{refl}\,\lambda$. We seek a line μ (see Figure 1.20) such that

(1)
$$A^{f \circ (\mathrm{refl}\,\lambda) \circ (\mathrm{refl}\,\mu)} = A, \text{ and}$$
$$B^{f \circ (\mathrm{refl}\,\lambda) \circ (\mathrm{refl}\,\mu)} = B.$$

The perpendicular bisector of line segment $BB^{f \circ \mathrm{refl}\,\lambda}$ will do for μ *provided* it contains A. But, surprisingly, this must be the case, for

$$\mathrm{dist}(A, B^{f \circ \mathrm{refl}\,\lambda}) = \mathrm{dist}(A^{f \circ \mathrm{refl}\,\lambda}, B^{f \circ \mathrm{refl}\,\lambda}) = \mathrm{dist}(A, B)$$

since the composition of two isometries is again an isometry. Thus, by (1.4.2) A is on the required perpendicular bisector.

Because of (1), the isometry $f \circ (\mathrm{refl}\,\lambda) \circ (\mathrm{refl}\,\mu)$ has (at least) two fixed

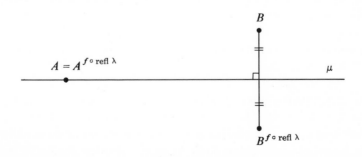

FIGURE 1.20

points. Therefore, by Proposition 1.4.1, this isometry must be either the identity or reflection in some line v.

Consider, first, the possibility $f \circ (\text{refl } \lambda) \circ (\text{refl } \mu) = \text{id}$. We can solve this for f by composing with refl μ on the right (which will cancel the factor refl μ) and then composing with refl λ on the right:

$$f = \text{id} \circ (\text{refl } \mu) \circ (\text{refl } \lambda).$$

Thus f is a composition of two reflections, as desired.

Finally, if $f \circ (\text{refl } \lambda) \circ (\text{refl } \mu) = \text{refl } v$, we again compose with refl μ and refl λ (both on the right) to obtain

$$f = (\text{refl } v) \circ (\text{refl } \mu) \circ (\text{refl } \lambda),$$

so that f is here a composition of three reflections. Thus the proof is complete. ☐

The above theorem has completed a big portion of the solution of our main problem of describing all isometries. Now, instead of having to describe them "abstractly" in terms of the equation $\text{dist}(A^f, B^f) = \text{dist}(A, B)$, we can describe them "concretely" as all possible combinations of two or three reflections in lines. The final answer, in a form easy to visualize, and beautifully simple to state, is:

1.4.8   CLASSIFICATION THEOREM FOR ISOMETRIES

Every isometry of the plane is either
(i) A rotation or a translation; or
(ii) A reflection in a line followed by a translation parallel to that line (this is called a *glide reflection*).

In the above theorem we allow the possibility of the *identity translation* and the *identity rotation*. In particular, this makes ordinary reflection a special case of glide reflection. *When a glide reflection has nonzero "glide" it can always be written in the form*

$$(\text{refl } AB) \circ (\text{trans } \overrightarrow{AB})$$

for two appropriately selected points A and B on its line of reflection.

Proof of the theorem.   Let an isometry f be given. By the previous theorem f can be expressed as the composition of two or three reflections in lines. If f is the composition of two reflections in lines, then it is a rotation if the lines meet and a translation if they are parallel (Corollaries 1.4.5 and 1.4.6).

Thus we only have to consider the case $f = (\text{refl } \lambda) \circ (\text{refl } \mu) \circ (\text{refl } \nu)$ where λ, μ, and ν are (arbitrary) given lines.

Consider, first, what happens when μ and ν meet in exactly one point A (see Figure 1.21). Recall that $(\text{refl } \mu) \circ (\text{refl } \nu)$ equals rotation, about A, through twice the directed angle θ from μ to ν (Corollary 1.4.5). Therefore, *if μ' and ν' are any lines containing A and such that the directed angle from μ to ν equals the directed angle from μ' to ν', then* $(\text{refl } \mu) \circ (\text{refl } \nu) =$ $= (\text{refl } \mu') \circ (\text{refl } \nu')$ [because both compositions equal $\text{rot}(A, 2\theta)$].

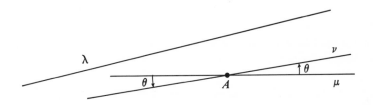

FIGURE 1.21

Let μ' be the line through A which is perpendicular to λ, and let ν' be the line through A at a directed angle of θ from μ' (Figure 1.22). Then $f = (\text{refl } \lambda) \circ (\text{refl } \mu) \circ (\text{refl } \nu) = (\text{refl } \lambda) \circ (\text{refl } \mu') \circ (\text{refl } \nu')$ because of the preceding paragraph. Now let λ'' be the line through B perpendicular to ν', and μ'' the line through B perpendicular to λ'' (Figure 1.23) so that, as before, $(\text{refl } \lambda) \circ (\text{refl } \mu') = (\text{refl } \lambda'') \circ (\text{refl } \mu'')$, and hence

(1) $f = (\text{refl } \lambda) \circ (\text{refl } \mu') \circ (\text{refl } \nu') = (\text{refl } \lambda'') \circ (\text{refl } \mu'') \circ (\text{refl } \nu')$.

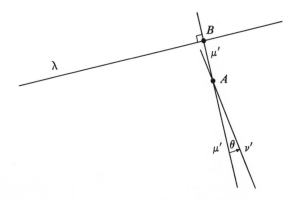

FIGURE 1.22

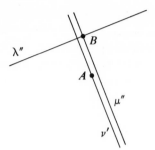

FIGURE 1.23

But since μ'' is parallel to v', $(\mathrm{refl}\ \mu'')\circ(\mathrm{refl}\ v')$ equals translation through twice the directed distance from μ'' to v' (Corollary 1.4.6). The direction of this translation, being perpendicular to μ'', is parallel to λ''. Thus (1) can be rewritten

$$f = (\mathrm{refl}\ \lambda'')\circ(\text{a translation parallel to } \lambda'')$$

as desired.

Problem 3. Write out the proof for the case that λ and μ meet at exactly one point.

Finally, we have to consider the case where λ is parallel to μ and μ is parallel to v (possibly two or three of these lines coincide) (Figure 1.24). First we note that *if λ' and μ' are lines parallel to λ and μ and such that the directed distance from λ to μ equals the directed distance from λ' to μ', then* $(\mathrm{refl}\ \lambda)\circ(\mathrm{refl}\ \mu) = (\mathrm{refl}\ \lambda')\circ(\mathrm{refl}\ \mu')$. This is true since, by Corollary 1.4.6, both compositions equal translation through twice the directed distance from λ to μ.

λ

μ

λ'

v

FIGURE 1.24

The way we use this is to let λ' be the line parallel to λ such that the directed distance from λ to μ equals the directed distance from λ' to v.

Then $f = (\text{refl } \lambda) \circ (\text{refl } \mu) \circ (\text{refl } v) = (\text{refl } \lambda') \circ (\text{refl } v) \circ (\text{refl } v) = \text{refl } \lambda'$ so that f is a reflection (followed by the identity translation). The proof of the classification theorem is now complete. ☐

Exercise. Let C be a point of a line λ. By factoring $\text{rot}(C, \theta)$ into the composition of two strategically chosen reflections, express $\text{rot}(C, \theta) \circ \text{refl } \lambda$ as a single reflection.

We close this section with some comments and problems which amplify and illustrate the classification theorem and its proof.

1.4.9   REMARK

If line segment AB is parallel to line λ (see Figure 1.25) then it is easy to see that $(\text{refl } \lambda) \circ (\text{trans } \overrightarrow{AB}) = (\text{trans } \overrightarrow{AB}) \circ (\text{refl } \lambda)$. Thus, in (ii) of the theorem, it doesn't make any difference whether the reflection part or translation part

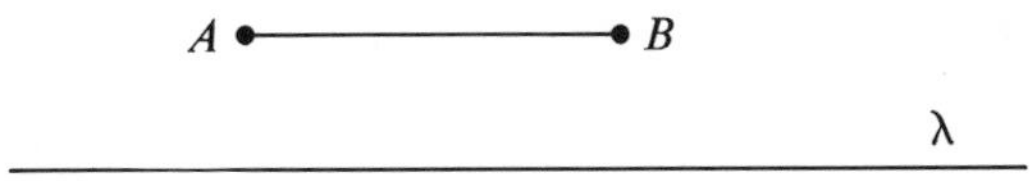

$$A \bullet\!\!\!\rule[0.35em]{8em}{0.4pt}\!\!\!\bullet B$$

$$\rule[0.35em]{18em}{0.4pt} \quad \lambda$$

FIGURE 1.25

of a glide reflection is done first. This "commutativity" property does not occur very often. In fact:

Problem 4. Let A and B be 2 distinct points and λ a line. Prove that

$$(\text{refl } \lambda) \circ (\text{trans } \overrightarrow{AB}) = (\text{trans } \overrightarrow{AB}) \circ (\text{refl } \lambda) \Leftrightarrow \begin{cases} \text{line segment } AB \\ \text{is parallel to } \lambda \end{cases} .$$

1.4.10   REMARK

In the classification theorem, rotations and translations were grouped together instead of being listed as separate possibilities. This was done for two reasons. The first is that one can (somewhat imprecisely) think of translation as the limiting case of a rotation, the center of the rotation being "infinitely far away". A second and more tangible reason can be given by means of the following definitions.

Let A, B, and C be non-collinear points. Then exactly one circle γ passes through them. If one must trace the circle γ in the counterclockwise direction to meet the points in the order A then B then C, we will say that *the points A, B, C have counterclockwise cyclic order*. A similar definition will apply to *clockwise cyclic order*. Figure 1.26 the points A, B, C have counterclockwise cyclic order, as do the points C, A, B. However the points A, C, B have clockwise cyclic order.

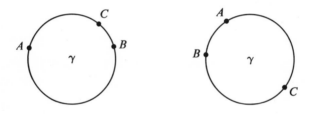

FIGURE 1.26

Let f be a function: (the plane) → (the plane). We will call f *direct* if for every three non-collinear points A, B, C which have counterclockwise cyclic order, so do the points A^f, B^f, C^f. (In particular, the latter three points are again non-collinear.) We will call f *opposite* if whenever non-collinear points A, B, C have *counter*clockwise cyclic order, then the points A^f, B^f, C^f have *clock*wise cyclic order. (In particular, they are again non-collinear.)

Examples of direct functions are translations and rotations; examples of opposite functions are reflections in lines. (But note that reflection in a *point* is a direct isometry.) Since the composition of a direct function and an opposite one must be opposite we see that glide reflections are opposite isometries. Thus, while an arbitrary function: (the plane) → (the plane) doesn't have to be either direct or opposite, a quick look at the classification theorem shows: *every isometry must be either direct or opposite.*

Suppose an isometry f is known to be a glide reflection but the instructions for computing f are given indirectly. (For example, the composition of a translation, a rotation, and a reflection is an opposite isometry; hence by the classification theorem it can be expressed as a glide reflection). How can one locate the line of reflection? If the "glide" is zero, then the line of reflection is merely the set of fixed points of f. But for the general case one must be more subtle:

Problem 5. Let A and B be points of a line λ and let f be the glide reflection $f = (\text{refl } \lambda) \circ (\text{trans } \overrightarrow{AB})$. (a) Show that, for every point P, the midpoint of line segment PP^f is a point of λ; and (b) every point Q of λ is the midpoint of some line segment PP^f. (c) Let f be the composition $f = (\text{trans } \overrightarrow{CD}) \circ \text{rot}(E, 30°) \circ (\text{refl } \mu)$. Use (a) and (b) to express f as a glide reflection. [To make a useable diagram possible, do (c) only for some particular choice of C, D, E, μ.]

Problem 6. Show that $(\text{trans } \overrightarrow{AB}) \circ \text{rot}(B, \theta) \circ (\text{trans } \overrightarrow{BA}) = \text{rot}(A, \theta)$. Use the answer to give a "2-line" solution to Problem 4 of Section 3.

Problem 7. Express, as a single translation, rotation, or glide reflection:

$$\text{trans}(\overrightarrow{AB}) \circ \text{rot}(B, \theta).$$

(*Hint.* Express each factor as a composition of strategically chosen reflections.)

Problem 8*. Express as a single translation, rotation, or glide reflection:

$$\text{rot}(C, \theta) \circ \text{rot}(D, \varphi) \qquad (C \neq D, 0 < \theta < 360°, 0 < \varphi < 360°).$$

(*Hint.* Express each factor as a product of reflections.)

(*Caution.* In Problem 8 there will be 2 distinct answers, depending on the given angles θ and φ.)

Problem 9. Complete Proposition 1.4.1 by listing which isometries can occur in (iii) and (iv).

Problem 10*. Let A, B, C and D be points with $\text{dist}(A, B) = \text{dist}(C, D) \neq 0$. Prove that there exist *exactly* 2 isometries f such that $A^f = C$ and $B^f = D$. (*Hint.* One will be direct, the other opposite.)

Problem 11*. Let $V_1, V_2, \ldots, V_n$ be successive vertices and $\theta_1, \theta_2, \ldots, \theta_n$ be the associated vertex angles (all $< 180°$) of an n-sided polygon, where n is *odd*. At each vertex V_i draw a circular arc A_iB_i of θ_i degrees counterclockwise (small enough so that no two of these arcs meet). Figure 1.27 illustrates the case $n = 7$.

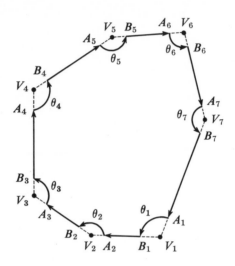

FIGURE 1.27

Express the following composition as a single, easily visualized isometry:

$$f = \text{rot}(V_1, \theta_1) \circ (\text{trans } \overrightarrow{B_1A_2}) \circ \text{rot}(V_2, \theta_2) \circ (\text{trans } \overrightarrow{B_2A_3}) \circ \ldots \circ \text{trans } \overrightarrow{B_nA_1}$$

(*Hints.* The answer will not depend on n or the particular angles θ_i. But f will *not* be the identity function.)

Problem 12. Prove that an isometry is direct if and only if it has a "square root" (g is a *square root* of f if $g \circ g = f$).

Problem 13. Let f and g be isometries and suppose A is a fixed point of both f and g. Then A is clearly a fixed point of $f \circ g$. Conversely, suppose A is a fixed point of $f \circ g$. Must it necessarily be a fixed point of f and of g?

Problem 14. Let α, β, and γ be lines whose intersections form a right triangle ABC whose hypotenuse AB is part of γ. Show that (refl γ) $\circ$

(refl β)∘(refl α) = (refl HC)∘(trans $\overrightarrow{HC}$) where $\overrightarrow{HC}$ is twice the altitude to the hypotenuse of $\triangle ABC$. (*Hint*. Use the procedure used in the proof of the classification theorem.)

1.5   SYMMETRIES AND THE ARITHMETIC OF ISOMETRIES

The statement, "The rectangle $\mathscr{R}$ is symmetric with respect to the dotted line λ", means that as a point P traces $\mathscr{R}$, so does the point $P^{\text{refl}\,\lambda}$. Hence

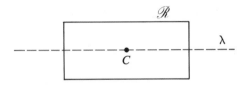

FIGURE 1.28

we can say, more briefly, that refl λ *is a symmetry* of $\mathscr{R}$. This is a special case of:

DEFINITION

Let $\mathscr{S}$ be a set of points in the plane. A *symmetry* of $\mathscr{S}$ is an isometry f of the plane such that $\mathscr{S}^f = \mathscr{S}$; that is, such that the set of points P^f, where P ranges through $\mathscr{S}$, is again $\mathscr{S}$.

The rectangle $\mathscr{R}$ above has exactly four symmetries: refl λ, reflection in the line through C perpendicular to λ, reflection in C [= rot$(C, 180°)$], and, of course, the identity isometry. A circle, on the other hand, has an infinite number of symmetries: all rotations centered at the center of the circle, and all reflections in lines containing the center of the circle.

The point C of the rectangle above is sometimes called its center of symmetry. We can make this notion precise as follows: P is a *center of symmetry* of a set $\mathscr{S}$ of points if P is a fixed point of every symmetry of $\mathscr{S}$. We will show in the next section, that every polygon which has at least two symmetries other than the identity has exactly one center of symmetry.

Again let $\mathscr{S}$ be any set of points of the plane, and let $\mathscr{G}$ be the set of all symmetries of $\mathscr{S}$. Note that $\mathscr{G}$ has the following properties:

(*G* id)   id belongs to $\mathscr{G}$.

(*G* ∘)   Whenever f and g belong to $\mathscr{G}$, so does $f \circ g$.

(*G* − 1) Whenever f belongs to $\mathscr{G}$, so does f^{-1}.

Any set $\mathscr{G}$ of isometries which has properties (*G* id), (*G* ∘), and (*G* − 1) will be called a *group* of isometries. [*Caution.* Because of this definition, the word "group" will no longer be interchangeable with "set", "collection", and "class".] We have already made considerable use of the fact that the set $\mathscr{G}$ of *all* isometries of the plane has these three "group properties".

1.5.1   PROPOSITION

A polygon[†] has only a finite number of symmetries, and each of these symmetries must be either a rotation or a reflection in a line.

Proof.   Let f be a symmetry of the given polygon $\mathscr{P}$. By the classification theorem for isometries (Section 1.4), f must be either a translation, rotation, or glide reflection. A translation can never be a symmetry of a polygon. Neither can a glide reflection h with nonzero "glide"; for if it were, then, by (*G* ∘), the nonzero translation $h \circ h$ would also be a symmetry of $\mathscr{P}$. Thus the only possibilities for f are rotation and reflection in a line.

Now let the number of vertices of $\mathscr{P}$ be n, and let A, B, and C be any three consecutive vertices of $\mathscr{P}$. Since an arbitrary symmetry f of $\mathscr{P}$ must be a rotation or a reflection, A^f, B^f, and C^f must again be consecutive vertices of $\mathscr{P}$. Thus there are at most n possibilities for B^f; for each of these there are at most two possibilities for C^f; and for each of these $\leq 2n$ possibilities there is no further choice for A^f. Since an isometry is completely determined by its effect on three non-collinear points (Corollary 1.4.4), f is completely determined by its effect on A, B, and C (which in our case means its effect on A and B).

Thus, *there are* $\leq 2n$ *symmetries of an n-sided polygon.* In particular, the number of these symmetries is finite.   ☐

[†] By a *polygon* $V_1 V_2 V_3 \ldots V_n$ we mean a finite number of distinct points $V_1, \ldots, V_n$ (the *vertices*) together with the line segments $V_1 V_2$, $V_2 V_3, \ldots$, $V_{n-1} V_n$, $V_n V_1$ provided that these line segments (called the *sides*) never meet except at their ends, where exactly two will meet at an angle $\neq 180°$. If we wish to include the area bounded by a polygon we will say *polygonal region*.

Exercise. Prove that $h \circ h$ in the proof above is indeed a nonzero translation.

1.5.2   REMARK

The proof of 1.5.1 actually provides a procedure for finding all symmetries of an n-sided polygon $\mathscr{P}$ with consecutive vertices $V_0, V_1, ..., V_{n-1}$:

(i) For each i find one symmetry f_i such that $V_0^{f_i} = V_i$ and $V_1^{f_i} = V_{i+1}$ (if there *is* one), and

(ii) For each i find one symmetry g_i such that $V_0^{g_i} = V_i$ and $V_1^{g_i} = V_{i-1}$ (if there *is* one).

The resulting symmetries will be *all* of the symmetries of $\mathscr{P}$.

Caution. In stating the above remark we have followed the convention that, when $i = n - 1$ in (i), $V_{(n-1)+1}$ means V_0 and (in (ii)) that $V_{0-1} = V_{n-1}$. This convention can be extended to $V_{n+1} = V_1$, $V_{n+2} = V_2, ...$ and $V_{-2} = V_{n-2}$, $V_3 = V_{n-3}, ...$. When we wish to call attention to this convention we will speak of *interpreting the subscripts mod n.*

A polygon will be called *regular* if its sides all have the same length and its interior angles are all equal.

Exercise. Find all symmetries of (a) an equilateral triangle, (b) a square, and (c) a regular pentagon.

1.5.3   EXAMPLE

Find all of the symmetries of an n-sided regular polygon $\mathscr{P}$ with consecutive vertices $V_0, V_1, ..., V_{n-1}$.

Let C be the center of $\mathscr{P}$ and note that the number of degrees in angle V_0CV_1 is $\theta = 360/n$, so that the rotation $r = \text{rot}(C, \theta)$ is a symmetry of $\mathscr{P}$ (see Figure 1.29 for the cases $n = 5$ and $n = 6$). Now let λ_0 be the line V_0C. Then refl λ_0 is a symmetry of $\mathscr{P}$. Letting $r^i = \text{rot}(C, i\theta)$ ($= r \circ r \circ ... \circ r$, with i "factors") we see that

$$V_0^{r^i} = V_i \quad \text{and} \quad V_1^{r^i} = V_{i+1} \quad \text{for} \quad i = 0, 1, 2, ..., n - 1.$$

Also,

$$V_0^{(\text{refl} \lambda_0) \circ r^i} = V_i \quad \text{and} \quad V_1^{(\text{refl} \lambda_0) \circ r^i} = V_{i-1} \quad \text{for} \quad i = 0, 1, ..., n - 1,$$

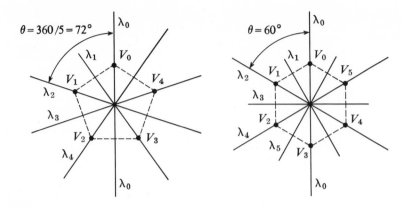

FIGURE 1.29

where r^0 is defined to be the identity ($= no$ rotation). Thus, by 1.5.2, the $2n$ symmetries listed above are *all* of the symmetries of $\mathscr{P}$. In order to visualize the last n of these more easily, let λ_i be the line through C, such that the directed angle from λ_0 to λ_i has $(\theta/2)i$ degrees ($i = 0, 1, ..., n-1$). Then (refl λ_0) $\circ$ (refl λ_i) = rot$(C, \theta i)$ = r^i. Hence

$$(\text{refl } \lambda_0) \circ r^i = (\text{refl } \lambda_0) \circ (\text{refl } \lambda_0) \circ (\text{refl } \lambda_i) = \text{refl } \lambda_i.$$

Thus we can describe all of the symmetries of $\mathscr{P}$ as follows:

(1) $r^0 (= \text{id}), r, r^2, r^3, ..., r^{n-1}$ ($r = \text{rot}(C, 360/n)$
refl λ_0, refl λ_1, ..., refl λ_{n-1} ($\lambda_0 = $ line V_0C; each λ_i $180/n$ degrees from the previous one.)

1.5.4   REMARKS

According to our previous discussion, the symmetries listed in (1) above must have the three group properties. Thus id appears in the list. What about r^{-1}? Since $r \circ r^{n-1} = r^n = \text{rot}(C, 360°) = \text{id}$ we see that $r^{n-1} = r^{-1}$. Similarly, $(r^i)^{-1} = r^{n-i}$ ($i = 0, ..., n-1$). Also each refl λ_i is its own inverse. What about compositions? For powers of r which exceed $n - 1$ the answer is easy: $r^2 \circ r^{n-1} = r^{n+1} = r$. For more complicated cases, see Problem 1 below.

Problem 1. Express each of the following compositions as one of the symmetries listed in (1) (i and $j = 0, 1, 2, ..., n-1$).

(i) $r \circ \text{refl } \lambda_0$ (iii) $(\text{refl } \lambda_j) \circ r^i$
(ii) $r^i \circ \text{refl } \lambda_j$ (iv) $(\text{refl } \lambda_i) \circ \text{refl } \lambda_j$

(*Answer to part* (iii). refl λ_{i+j}, the subscripts to be interpreted mod n.)

Problem 2. Find all symmetries of the regular 6-pointed star (Figure 1.30). (Each triangle $V_i V_{i+1} V_{i+2}$ is equilateral and hexagon $V_1 V_3 V_5 V_7 V_9 V_{11}$ is regular.)

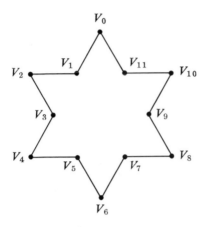

FIGURE 1.30

Problem 3*. Let $\mathscr{S}$ be the grid formed by ruling the plane with an infinite number of equally-spaced horizontal and vertical lines, the "equal spacing" being 1 unit (Figure 1.31). Find all symmetries of $\mathscr{S}$. (A modification of the procedure of 1.5.2 will be necessary because there will be an infinite number of symmetries.)

(*Hint*. The answer will include translations, rotations, and glide reflections. All of the rotations will be centered at a vertex of $\mathscr{S}$, or at the cen-

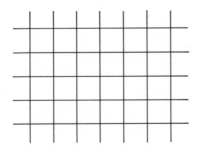

FIGURE 1.31

ter of one of the 1×1 squares of $\mathscr{S}$, or at the midpoint of one of the sides of such a square. All of the lines of the glide reflections will be horizontal, or vertical, or at 45° to these directions.)

Problem 4*. Let $\mathscr{P}$ be a polygon with n vertices $V_0, \ldots, V_{n-1}$ and suppose that $\mathscr{P}$ has exactly $2n$ symmetries. Is $\mathscr{P}$ *necessarily* regular?

REVIEW PROBLEMS

Problem 5. Let A be a point, λ a line, and $0 < \theta < 360°$. Show that

$$\mathrm{rot}(A, \theta) \circ \mathrm{refl}\,\lambda = (\mathrm{refl}\,\lambda) \circ \mathrm{rot}(A, \theta) \Leftrightarrow \begin{cases} \theta = 180°, \text{ and} \\ A \text{ is a point of } \lambda. \end{cases}$$

Problem 6. Let $r(A) = \mathrm{rot}(A, 180°)$, that is, reflection in the point A. Prove that, for distinct non-collinear points A, B, C, D:

$$r(A) \circ r(B) \circ r(C) \circ r(D) = \mathrm{id} \Leftrightarrow \begin{cases} A, B, C, D \text{ are consecutive} \\ \text{vertices of a parallelogram}. \end{cases}$$

(*Hint.* First show $r(A) \circ r(B) = \mathrm{trans}(\text{twice } \overrightarrow{AB})$).

Problem 7. Express $(\mathrm{refl}\,\lambda_1) \circ (\mathrm{refl}\,\lambda_2) \circ (\mathrm{refl}\,\lambda_3) \circ (\mathrm{refl}\,\lambda_4)$ in simplest form, where the four lines of reflection all meet at a point A at the angles shown in Figure 1.32.

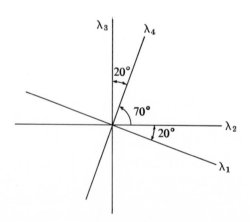

FIGURE 1.32

Problem 8. Let $f = (\text{refl } AB) \circ (\text{trans } \overrightarrow{AB})$ and $g = (\text{refl } CD) \circ (\text{trans } \overrightarrow{CD})$ where line AB is *not* parallel to line CD. Show that $f \circ g$ is a rotation and find the angle of this rotation in terms of A, B, C, and D. (*Hint*. Problem 7 of Section 1.4 and its variant with the rotation occurring first will help.)

1.6　　MORE ABOUT SYMMETRIES

In the previous section we saw that each polygon has only a finite number of symmetries, that each of these symmetries must be a rotation or a reflection (or the identity) and that the set of all symmetries of the polygon forms a group. Now consider the converse question: *What properties must a finite set of isometries have before we can conclude that it is the set of all symmetries of some polygon?* Surprisingly little, namely:

1.6.1　THEOREM

Let $\mathscr{G}$ be a finite set of isometries and suppose that whenever f and g belong to $\mathscr{G}$ so does $f \circ g$. Then $\mathscr{G}$ is the set of all symmetries of some polygon.

The proof of this deceptively simple-looking theorem will occupy almost all of this section, partly as problems. We begin with:

1.6.2　LEMMA

The $\mathscr{G}$ of Theorem 1.6.1 must be a group.

Proof. We have to prove that id belongs to $\mathscr{G}$ (property $(G \text{ id})$); and for every f in $\mathscr{G}$, f^{-1} belongs to $\mathscr{G}$ (property $(G-1)$). Let the number of elements of $\mathscr{G}$ be n, so that we can write the elements of $\mathscr{G}$ in the form $g_1, g_2, \ldots, g_n$.
Now consider the isometries

$$(1) \qquad g_1 \circ g_1, \quad g_1 \circ g_2, \quad g_1 \circ g_3, \quad \ldots, \quad g_1 \circ g_n$$

which, by hypothesis, belong to $\mathscr{G}$. No two of them can be the same: if $g_1 \circ g_i = g_1 \circ g_j$, then composing with g_1^{-1} on the left shows $g_i = g_j$. Thus (1) contains n different elements of the n-element set $\mathscr{G}$; in other words (1) lists each element of $\mathscr{G}$ exactly once. In particular, g_1 must occur in the list, say

$g_1 \circ g_i = g_1$. Then composing on the left with g_1^{-1} shows that $g_i = g_1^{-1} \circ g_1 = $ id. Thus id is an element of $\mathscr{G}$.

Since id belongs to $\mathscr{G}$, it must also occur in (1), say $g_1 \circ g_j = $ id. Composing on the left with g_1^{-1} then shows $g_j = g_1^{-1}$ so that g_1^{-1} also belongs to $\mathscr{G}$. Similarly, so do $g_2^{-1}, g_3^{-1}, ..., g_n^{-1}$, so the proof is complete. (For g_2^{-1}, consider $g_2 \circ g_1, \quad g_2 \circ g_2, \quad ..., \quad g_2 \circ g_n$). $\square$

DEFINITION

A translation or rotation will be called *proper* if it $\neq$ the identity.

1.6.3   LEMMA

Let $\mathscr{G}$ be a group of isometries containing at least one proper rotation centered at each of two distinct points A and B. Then either

(i) $\mathscr{G}$ contains a proper translation; or

(ii) $\mathscr{G}$ contains proper rotations centered at 2 points C and D, one on each side of line AB (Figure 1.33).

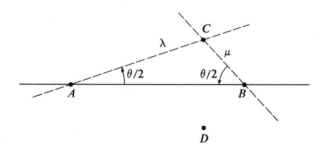

FIGURE 1.33

Proof. Let $r = \text{rot}(A, \theta)$ belong to $\mathscr{G}$, where $\theta \neq 0$. We can suppose that either $-180° < \theta < 0°$ or $0 < \theta \leq 180°$. If the first possibility holds, then (since $\mathscr{G}$ is a group) $r^{-1} = \text{rot}(A, -\theta)$ is an element of $\mathscr{G}$ with $0 < -\theta < 180°$. Thus, after interchanging the names of θ and $-\theta$, if necessary, we obtain $0 < \theta \leq 180°$. Similarly there is a rotation $\text{rot}(B, \varphi)$ in $\mathscr{G}$ with $0 < \varphi \leq 180°$.

Let λ be the line through A such that the directed angle from line AB to λ is $\theta/2$. Since $0 < \theta \leq 180°$, we have $0 < \theta/2 \leq 90°$ (see the Figure 1.33).

By Corollary 1.4.5,

(1) $\text{rot}(A, \theta) = (\text{refl }AB) \circ \text{refl }\lambda.$

Similarly, define μ to be the line through B such that the directed angle from μ to AB is $\varphi/2$. As before $0 < \varphi/2 \leq 90°$ and

(2) $\text{rot}(B, \varphi) = (\text{refl }\mu) \circ \text{refl }AB.$

Since $\mathcal{G}$ is a group, the composition $\text{rot}(B, \varphi) \circ \text{rot}(A, \theta)$ is an element of $\mathcal{G}$, and (1) and (2) show

(3) $\text{rot}(B, \varphi) \circ \text{rot}(A, \theta) = (\text{refl }\mu) \circ (\text{refl }AB) \circ (\text{refl }AB) \circ (\text{refl }\lambda)$
$= (\text{refl }\mu) \circ (\text{refl }\lambda).$

Now, if (unlike the diagram) λ and μ are parallel, then this last composition is a translation (Corollary 1.4.6), giving (i). If they are not parallel, then the point C where they meet is *above* line AB (since $0 < \theta/2 \leq 90°$ and $0 < \varphi/2 \leq \leq 90°$) and the composition in (3) is rotation, centered at C through twice the directed angle from μ to λ, giving half of (ii).

To obtain a rotation centered at a point D below line AB (namely $D = C^{\text{refl }AB}$) work with $-\theta/2$ and $-\varphi/2$ instead of $\theta/2$ and $\varphi/2$. This completes the proof. □

1.6.4   EXERCISE

Prove every finite group of isometries consists wholly of proper rotations, reflections in lines, and the identity. (*Hint.* See the proof of 1.5.1. Note that no claim is made that all three actually occur in every finite group of isometries.)

1.6.5   PROPOSITION

Every finite group $\mathcal{G}$ of isometries has at least one fixed point F (that is, such that $F^f = F$ for every f in $\mathcal{G}$).

Proof.   Since $\mathcal{G}$ consists wholly of rotations and reflections, our assertion amounts to saying that F is the center of every proper rotation in $\mathcal{G}$ and lies on the line of every reflection in $\mathcal{G}$. Therefore it will be sufficient to prove the following three statements:
(1) All of the proper rotations in $\mathcal{G}$ (if any) have the same center.

(2) If $\mathscr{G}$ contains at least 2 reflections, then all of the lines of reflections in $\mathscr{G}$ meet in a common point.

(3) If $\mathscr{G}$ contains at least one proper rotation and one reflection, then each line of reflection must pass through the center of each rotation.

We now prove (1). Suppose, to the contrary, that (1) were false, and let $A_1, A_2, ..., A_n$ be all of the points which are centers of proper rotations in $\mathscr{G}$. Our supposition is then that $n \geq 2$. Let v be any horizontal line *above* all the points $A_1, ..., A_n$. Move the line v down (keeping it horizontal) until the first time it reaches some point A_i, and call the horizontal line through A_i v'. Rotate v' counterclockwise about A_i, if necessary, until the first time it reaches some point A_j with $j \neq i$, and call this last line v'' (Figure 1.34).

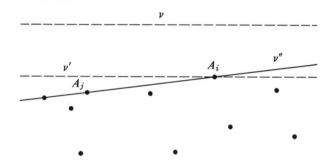

FIGURE 1.34

This line v'' has two properties which interest us: It contains the centers $A = A_j$ and $B = A_i$ of two distinct proper rotations of $\mathscr{G}$; and all those rotations in $\mathscr{G}$ whose centers A_k lie off v'' have their centers on the *same side* of v'' (in Figure 1.34 these centers are below v''). But then Lemma 1.6.3 shows that $\mathscr{G}$ contains a proper translation, an impossibility for a finite group of isometries (1.6.4).

This contradiction shows that our unproved supposition "$n \geq 2$" must have been wrong. Hence $n = 1$ or 0 and (1) is proved. The proof is completed in Problems 1 and 2 below. □

Problem 1. Prove (2). (*Hint.* Reduce to (1) by composing reflections to obtain rotations.)

Problem 2. Prove (3). (*Hint.* Prove that $(\text{refl } \lambda) \circ \text{rot}(A, \theta) \circ \text{refl } \lambda = \text{rot}(A^{\text{refl} \lambda}, -\theta)$ and then reduce to (1).)

We can now find all finite groups of isometries. We consider several cases according to the number of reflections in the group. The first case is that of no reflections.

1.6.6　　PROPOSITION

Let $\mathscr{G}$ be a finite group of $n \geq 2$ isometries and suppose that $\mathscr{G}$ consists wholly of rotations. Then $\mathscr{G}$ must consist merely of the powers of a single rotation. More completely, $\mathscr{G}$ consists of

$$r^0 (= \text{id}), r, r^2, ..., r^{n-1} \quad \text{where} \quad r = \text{rot}(C, 360°/n)$$

for some point C.

Before beginning the proof we solve a problem which illustrates its meaning. *Let C be a point. Find the smallest group $\mathscr{G}$ of isometries which contains* rot$(C, 120°)$ *and* rot$(C, 180°)$.

Since $\mathscr{G}$ contains rot$(C, 120°)$ it also contains the square of this; that is, rot$(C, 240°)$. $\mathscr{G}$ must also contain rot$(C, 120°) \circ \text{rot}(C, 180°) = \text{rot}(C, 300°)$ and hence also rot$(C, 300°)^{-1} = \text{rot}(C, 60°)$. Thus, if we let $r = \text{rot}(C, 60°)$ we see that $\mathscr{G}$ contains

$$\text{id}, r, r^2, r^3, r^4, r^5$$

and since these six rotations form a group, this group must be $\mathscr{G}$.

Note that $\mathscr{G}$ *consists of powers of a single rotation*, as claimed in (1.6.6).

Proof of (1.6.6). Since every finite group of isometries must have a fixed point (1.6.5), it follows that all of the rotations in our given group $\mathscr{G}$ must have the same center. Call this common center C.

Problem 3*. Complete the proof. (*Hints.* Let θ be the smallest positive number of degrees such that $r = \text{rot}(C, \theta)$ belongs to $\mathscr{G}$. Then so do all of the powers $r^0 (= \text{id}), r, r^2, r^3, ...$. Let n be the smallest positive integer such that $n\theta \geq 360°$ and prove that $n\theta = 360°$.)　□

1.6.7　　REMARK

We now relate the previous proposition to our main problem by observing: *Any group consisting of $n - 1$ proper rotations and the identity $(n \geq 2)$ is the group of all symmetries of a 2n-sided ratchet polygon* (defined below).

To avoid excessive notation, we give the definition of a *ratchet 2n-gon* only for $n = 6$. Draw a regular hexagon $V_0V_2V_4V_6V_8V_{10}$ with center C (see Figure 1.35). Then choose V_1 on line CV_0 extended through V_0. Finally, choose V_3, V_5, V_7, V_9, V_{11} outside the hexagon such that triangles $V_0V_1V_2$, $V_2V_3V_4$, $V_4V_5V_6$,... are all congruent and the triples of points CV_2V_3, CV_4V_5,... are each collinear.

The rotations which are symmetries of this ratchet 12-gon are clearly

$$r^0, r, r^2, r^3, r^4, r^5 \quad \text{where} \quad r = \text{rot}(C, 60°).$$

No reflection in a line can be a symmetry of this 12-gon since such a reflection would reverse the counterclockwise cyclic order of V_0, V_1, V_2.

The case $n \neq 6$ is handled similarly except for the case $n = 2$. Here we will agree to stretch our imagination and define a ratchet 4-gon to be a parallelogram which is neither a rectangle nor a rhombus (Figure 1.36).[†] The symmetries of this parallelogram are id and rot$(C, 180°)$. □

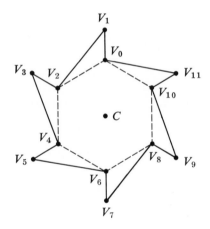

FIGURE 1.35

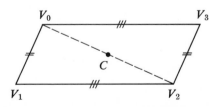

FIGURE 1.36

† A *rhombus* is a parallelogram whose sides all have equal length.

1.6.8   PROPOSITION

If a finite group of isometries contains at least two reflections (in lines) then it must be the group of all symmetries of some regular polygon or of a rhombus.

Proof. Let $\mathscr{G}$ be the given group. Since $\mathscr{G}$ must have a fixed point C (Proposition 1.6.5) the lines of the two given reflections must meet at C, and hence $\mathscr{G}$ contains their composition, which is a proper rotation (Corollary 1.4.5).

    Let $\mathscr{R}$ be the set of all rotations in $\mathscr{G}$ (including id), and let n be the number of isometries in $\mathscr{R}$. Then $n \geq 2$. Since C is a fixed point for all of $\mathscr{G}$, it is the common center for all the proper rotations in $\mathscr{R}$. It is now easy to check that $\mathscr{R}$ is a *group* of isometries. Hence (Proposition 1.6.6) $\mathscr{R}$ consists of

(1) $r^0 (= \text{id}), r, r^2, r^3, ..., r^{n-1}$ where $r = \text{rot}(C, 360°/n) = \text{rot}(C, \theta)$.

Next, let λ_0 be one of the lines of reflection in $\mathscr{G}$, and recall that λ_0 passes through C, the fixed point of $\mathscr{G}$. Writing r in the form $(\text{refl } \lambda_0) \circ \text{refl } \lambda_1$ where λ_1 is the line through C such that the directed angle from λ_0 to λ_1 is $\theta/2$, we see that

$$(\text{refl } \lambda_0) \circ r = (\text{refl } \lambda_0) \circ (\text{refl } \lambda_0) \circ (\text{refl } \lambda_1) = \text{refl } \lambda_1$$

so that refl λ_1 belongs to $\mathscr{G}$. Giving this same treatment to $(\text{refl } \lambda_1) \circ r$ we see that the following reflections belong to $\mathscr{G}$.

(2)   refl λ_0, refl λ_1, ..., refl λ_{n-1} (each λ_i is $\theta/2$ degrees from the previous one)

Perhaps Figure 1.37, showing the case $n = 6$, will help us to visualize (1) and (2). If we now compare equations (1) and (2) with equation (1) of Example 1.5.3, we see that $\mathscr{G}$ contains all of the symmetries of some regular n-gon, *provided $n \geq 3$*. For $n = 2$ it is easy to see that (1) and (2) describe all of the symmetries of a rhombus. Thus, to complete the proof it will be sufficient to show that every reflection in $\mathscr{G}$ appears in (2).

    To do this, let λ' be the line of some additional purported reflection in $\mathscr{G}$. Then λ' must pass through C, as does every line of reflection in $\mathscr{G}$. Hence λ' must lie between some λ_i and the next, so the directed angle φ from λ_i to λ' satisfies $0 < \varphi < \theta/2 = 180/n = $ the angle from each λ_i to the next. Then the rotation

(3) $(\text{refl } \lambda_i) \circ (\text{refl } \lambda') = \text{rot}(C, 2\varphi)$

belongs to $\mathscr{G}$. But $360/n$ is the smallest positive number of degrees in a rotation belonging to $\mathscr{G}$ (by (1)). Hence the inequality $0 < 2\varphi < \theta = 360/n$,

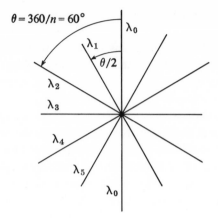

FIGURE 1.37

yields a contradiction. This shows that the "additional reflection" could not exist, and completes the proof of the proposition. $\square$

We have now proved the following cases of the main theorem (1.6.1): (i) $\mathcal{G}$ contains ≥ 2 reflections (1.6.8), and (ii) $\mathcal{G}$ contains *no* reflections and has ≥ 1 proper rotation. This leaves the cases (iii) $\mathcal{G}$ contains no reflections and no proper rotations, and (iv) $\mathcal{G}$ contains exactly one reflection, and possibly some rotations.

In (iii), $\mathcal{G}$ must consist of the identity alone (1.6.4), and hence is the group of all symmetries of any triangle whose sides all have different lengths.

Problem 4. Complete the proof of Theorem 1.6.1 by showing:

1.6.9   PROPOSITION

If the number of reflections contained in a finite group $\mathcal{G}$ of isometries equals 1, then $\mathcal{G}$ must be the group of all symmetries of a strictly[†] isosceles triangle.

[†] This means that two sides, but not all three, have equal length.

1.6.10   REMARKS

The long sequence of proofs in this section can be used to establish more than merely Theorem 1.6.1. We close this section with three additional consequences. *Let $\mathscr{P}$ be any polygon. Then there is a regular polygon or a ratchet polygon or a rhombus or a triangle whose symmetries are exactly the same as those of $\mathscr{P}$.*

To see this, let $\mathscr{G}$ be the group of all symmetries of $\mathscr{P}$. Then $\mathscr{G}$ is a finite group (1.5.1) and hence it must be one of the groups of symmetries enumerated in the proof of Theorem 1.6.1; that is, precisely those claimed.

This property is illustrated by the polygon in Figure 1.38 whose set of symmetries coincides with that of an appropriately chosen square.

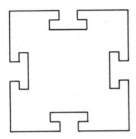

FIGURE 1.38

For the second consequence, recall that a *center of symmetry* of a figure is a point in the plane which is fixed by every symmetry of the figure. We will call a center of symmetry *proper* if the figure has only one center of symmetry. Thus a strictly isosceles triangle has an infinite number of centers of symmetry (any point on the median to the base) and therefore does not have a proper center of symmetry.

1.6.11   THEOREM

Every polygon with at least two symmetries $\neq$ id has a proper center of symmetry.

Proof. The set of symmetries of the polygon is a finite group (1.5.1) and hence has a fixed point (1.6.5) C. C is a center of symmetry of the polygon.

Since 2 isometries, each of which must be a rotation or a reflection (1.6.4 or 1.5.1) can have at most one fixed point in common, the center of symmetry C must be proper. □

Quick proofs such as the above once prompted S. Cairns to observe that any proof is short if you start close enough to the end!

Finally, we note that *if a polygon $\mathscr{P}$ has at least two symmetries $\neq$ id, then its symmetries must themselves be symmetrically arranged.* For the set $\mathscr{G}$ of symmetries of $\mathscr{P}$ is a finite group. If $\mathscr{G}$ contains at least two reflections, then all the lines of reflections must be equally spaced around a common point (the proof of 1.6.8); and whether or not $\mathscr{G}$ contains reflections, its rotations are evenly distributed around the circle (1.6.8 and 1.6.6).

Problem 5. A group is called *commutative* if $g \circ h = h \circ g$ for every g and h in the group. Otherwise the group is called *non-commutative.* Prove that a finite group of isometries is non-commutative if and only if it is the group of all symmetries of some *regular* polygon.

Problem 6. Let ..., A_{-3}, A_{-2}, A_{-1}, A_0, A_1, A_2, A_3,... be an infinite number of points equally spaced along a straight line as in Figure 1.39.

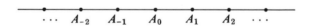

$$\cdots \quad A_{-2} \quad A_{-1} \quad A_0 \quad A_1 \quad A_2 \quad \cdots$$

FIGURE 1.39

Does the following set of isometries form a group?

$$\begin{cases} \text{id} \\ ..., \text{rot}(A_{-1}, 180°), \text{rot}(A_0, 180°), \text{rot}(A_1, 180°), ... \\ \text{trans } \overrightarrow{A_i A_{i+2j}} \text{ where } i \text{ and } j = ..., -3, -2, -1, 0, 1, 2, 3, ... \end{cases}$$

Problem 7*. Is the following variant of Lemma 1.6.3 true or false? Every group of isometries which contains proper rotations about each of 2 distinct points must contain proper rotations about an infinite number of points.

---

2 | Geometry of the Complex Numbers

2.1   INTRODUCTION

The number system with which young children first become acquainted is the system of positive integers (1, 2, 3,...). This number system eventually becomes inadequate because it doesn't contain solutions to equations of the form $nx = m$. (Of course, this is usually expressed less algebraically in some such form as, "How do you divide 5 apples equally among 3 people?".) To remedy this situation, fractions are placed between the positive integers and we obtain the set of *positive rational numbers*, that is, numbers of the form m/n with m and n positive integers. The system is soon enlarged again, by the addition of 0 and negative numbers, to become the set of *rational numbers*.

The set of rational numbers still has "holes" in it, however. For example, there is no rational number (positive or negative) x such that

$x^2 = 3$. (This statement is certainly not obvious. However the details of its proof would take us too far afield from the main purpose of this chapter. But see Corollary 7.4 and Problem 2 of Chapter 7.) To remedy this situation the set of rational numbers is again enlarged to become the set of real numbers. (A *real number* is any number which can be written as the sum of an integer—positive, negative, or zero—and a decimal. $a_1a_2a_3\ldots$, possibly containing an infinite number of decimal places.) In the set of real numbers, the equation $x^2 = 3$ now has 2 solutions—a positive one beginning $1.732\ldots$, and the negative of this. In fact, it can be proved that every equation $x^n = b$ (n a positive integer, b a positive real number) has a solution in the real numbers, and that every equation $a_nx^n + a_{n-1}x^{n-1} + \cdots + a_1x + a_0 = 0$ (each a_j a real number and $a_n \neq 0$) of *odd* degree n has at least one solution in the real number system.

However, some equations of even degree do not have solutions. For example, the simple quadratic equation $x^2 = -1$ has no solution among the real numbers because the square of a real number must be positive or zero. To remedy this situation we invent a new number i such that $i^2 = -1$ and use this to enlarge the set of real numbers to become the set of *complex numbers*, the subject of this chapter.

The main difficulty in this last enlargement is where to "put" the new number i. It can be neither positive nor negative since then its square would have to be positive. We resolve this difficulty by a simple geometrical device. Introduce a rectangular coordinate system, calling the horizontal axis the *real axis* and the vertical axis the *imaginary axis*. Then to the point whose coordinates are (x, y)—with x and y real numbers—we give the alternative name $x + yi$ (sometimes $x + iy$ when more convenient). Figure 2.1 shows the sample points $3 + 2i$, $3 - 2i$, $1 = 1 + 0i$, and $i = 0 + 1i$.

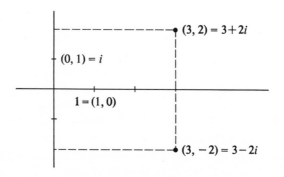

FIGURE 2.1

Thus the *complex numbers* are a way of labelling points of the Euclidean plane with symbols of the form $x + yi$, where x and y are real numbers. We will call x the *real part* of $x + yi$, and y its *imaginary part*. If $x = 0$ we will write yi instead of $0 + yi$ and call yi a *purely imaginary* number (to conform to historical usage which indicates some mistrust of the complex numbers). Note that the imaginary part of the purely imaginary number $3i$ is the *real* number 3.

2.2   ARITHMETIC OPERATIONS

So far we have defined the *set* of complex numbers. To make this set into a number system we must define addition and multiplication.

DEFINITIONS

Let $A = a + bi$ and $C = c + di$ (a, b, c, d real) be complex numbers. Then we define the *sum* $A + C$ to be the number obtained by separately adding the real and imaginary parts of A and C:

$$A + C = (a + c) + (b + d) i .$$

We define the *product* AC to be the result of "multiplying out" the 2 binomials $a + bi$ and $c + di$, setting $i^2 = -1$, and then collecting real and imaginary parts as follows:

$$AC = (a + bi)(c + di) = ac + bci + adi + bdi^2$$
$$= (ac - bd) + (bc + ad) i .$$

The following simple exercises will illustrate the above definitions.

Exercise 1. Express each of the following in the form $x + yi$. Draw a diagram for each computation and save the diagrams for reference later in this chapter.

    (a) $(-2 + i) + (3 + 2i)$ (b) $(-2 + i)(3 + 2i)$
    (c) $(3 + 4i)(3/25 - (4/25) i)$

    (d) $(a + bi)\left(\dfrac{a}{a^2 + b^2} - \dfrac{b}{a^2 + b^2} i \right)$ $(a^2 + b^2 \neq 0)$.

(*Answers.*   (a) $1 + 3i$, (b) $-8 - i$, (c) 1, (d) 1.)

Exercise 2. Let A, C, and E be complex numbers. It is always true that $AC = CA$? That $(AC)E = A(CE)$? That $A(B + C) = AB + AC$?

(*Answers.*   Yes. Yes. Yes.)

We have defined addition and multiplication of complex numbers purely algebraically. Is there a way to visualize these operations geometrically? The diagram for Exercise 1(a) is Figure 2.2.

2.2.1   THEOREM

Let $A = a + bi$ and $C = c + di$ (a, b, c, d real) be complex numbers ($=$ points in the plane) such that the points 0, A, and C are *not collinear*. Then $A + C$ is the point in the plane such that 0, A, $A + C$, C are consecutive vertices of a parallelogram. When 0, A, and C are collinear, then $A + C$ is collinear with them.

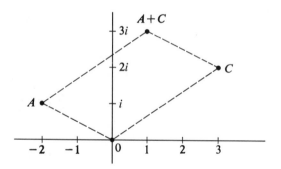

FIGURE 2.2

Problem 1. Prove the theorem.

2.2.2   COROLLARY

Let A, C, and E be complex numbers. Then

   (i) $A + C = A^{\text{trans } \overrightarrow{0C}}$

   (ii) $E - C = 0^{\text{trans } \overrightarrow{CE}}$

Exercise. Prove the corollary. (Note that the symbol $\overrightarrow{CE}$ does *not* indicate any multiplication.)

In order to visualize a product of complex numbers, we have to work a little harder. [See the diagram you made for Exercise 1(b).]

DEFINITIONS

For a complex number $A = a + bi \neq 0$ the *polar angle* of A is the directed angle, from the positive real axis to the directed line segment $\overrightarrow{OA} (= \theta$ in the diagrams). As usual, a positive number of degrees indicates measurement in the counterclockwise direction.

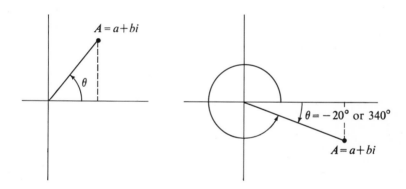

FIGURE 2.3

Caution. Note that, in Figure 2.3, the polar angle of A is measured in two different ways: as $-20°$ and also as $+340°$. The measure of this angle could also have been given as $710°(= 340° + 360°)$—in fact by $340° + (360°)n$ for *any* integer n.)

The *absolute value* of A is the nonnegative real number $|A| = \sqrt{a^2 + b^2}$. By the Pythagorean theorem, $|A|$ *equals the undirected distance between* 0 *and* A.

Note that $a/|A| = \cos\theta$ and $b/|A| = \sin\theta$. Hence:

2.2.3   PROPOSITION

Let θ be the polar angle of a complex number $A \neq 0$. Then

$$A = |A|(\cos \theta + i \sin \theta).$$

We will call this the *polar form* of A.

Exercise. Using trigonometric tables express the numbers $3 \pm 4i$ and $-1 + i\sqrt{3}$ in polar form with θ to the nearest degree. Check your answer by using graph paper to draw the points.

Exercise. Establish the following formula, which we will use often in later chapters.

$$\text{dist}(A, B) = |A - B|$$

Problem 2. Show that every complex number $A \neq 0$ can be written in the form $A = dE$ where d is positive and real and $|E| = 1$. If $A = d'E'$ is also a factorization with d' positive and real and $|E'| = 1$, is it *necessarily* true that $d = d'$ and $E = E'$? (*Hint.* For the first part use the proposition.)

2.2.4   THEOREM

Let A and C be complex numbers $\neq 0$. Then AC is the complex number whose absolute value is the product of the absolute values of A and C, and whose polar angle is the *sum* of the polar angles of A and C.

Proof.   Write A and C in polar form $A = |A|(\cos \theta + i \sin \theta)$, $C = |C|(\cos \varphi + i \sin \varphi)$. Then multiply

$$AC = |A|\,|C|\,(\cos \theta + i \sin \theta)(\cos \varphi + i \sin \varphi)$$
$$= |A|\,|C|\,[(\cos \theta \cos \varphi - \sin \theta \sin \varphi) + i(\sin \theta \cos \varphi + \cos \theta \sin \varphi)].$$

Note that the two expressions in parentheses are the formulas for $\cos(\theta + \varphi)$ and $\sin(\theta + \varphi)$. Therefore,

$$(1) \qquad\qquad AC = |A|\,|C|\,[\cos(\theta + \varphi) + i \sin(\theta + \varphi)]$$

Proposition 2.2.3 states that the complex number whose absolute value is $|A||C|$ and whose polar angle is $\theta + \varphi$ is the right-hand side of (1), and hence equals AC.   □

Problem 3. (a) Let line segments of length r and s and one of unit length 1 be given. Give a "ruler and compass" construction for a line segment of length rs. (*Hint.* Let $x = rs$. Then $x/s = r/1$.)

(b) Use (a) to construct the product $(-2 + i)(3 + 2i)$ with ruler and compass. Compare your answer with that of Exercise 1(b).

Problem 4. Give a geometric description of the point function f defined by $P^f = P^2/|P|$ (P a complex number). (*Hint.* First draw P, then P^2, then P^f.)

We now specialize Theorem 2.2.4 to find a "geometric explanation" of. the assertion $i^2 = -1$. The polar form of i is $i = 1(\cos 90° + i \sin 90°)$. Thus, by the theorem, $i^2 = ii$ is the complex number whose absolute value is 1 and whose polar angle is $90° + 90°$; that is $i^2 = -1$. Therefore "$i^2 = -1$" is merely an algebraic way of stating that the sum of two right angles is a straight angle.

Exercise. Give the "geometric explanation" of $i^4 = +1$ and $(-1)^2 = = +1$.

We close the chapter with several illustrations of ways in which the geometry of the complex numbers can shed light on their arithmetic. For the first of these, note that part of the assertion of Theorem 2.4 is $|AC| = = |A| \cdot |C|$. Letting $A = a + bi$ so that $|A|^2 = a^2 + b^2$, and $C = c + di$ so that $|C|^2 = c^2 + d^2$ we see that $|AC| =$

$$(ac - bd)^2 + (bc + ad)^2 = (a^2 + b^2)(c^2 + d^2)$$

for any real numbers a, b, c, and d. This can, of course, be verified directly.

2.2.5 COROLLARY

For every complex number $A \neq 0$ there is exactly one complex number C such that $AC = 1$.

Proof. Let $A = |A|(\cos \theta + i \sin \theta)$, and let $C = (1/|A|)[\cos(-\theta) + + i \sin(-\theta)]$. Then by Theorem 2.2.4 the absolute value of AC is $|A| \times (1/|A|) = 1$ and its polar angle is $\theta - \theta = 0$. Hence $AC = 1(\cos 0 + i \sin 0) = 1$.

There is no other such number C, for if we write $C = |C|(\cos \varphi + i \sin \varphi)$, then Theorem 2.2.4 together with $AC = 1$ shows that $|A||C| = 1$ and $\theta + \varphi = 0$. (Actually $\theta + \varphi = 0 + (360°)n$ so $\varphi = -\theta + (360°)n$. But all these values of the angle *measure* φ give the same *angle* φ.) ▯

As with real numbers, we use the notation $1/A$ for the number C of Corollary 2.2.5. We can now define the quotient E/A of two complex numbers to be E times the complex number $1/A$.

Exercise. Find the absolute value and polar angle of E/A in terms of those of E and A. (*Answer.* $|E/A| = |E|/|A|$ and polar angle $(E/A) =$ = polar angle (E) − polar angle (A).) Use this to show that $EG/AG =$ = E/A (E, A, G all $\neq 0$). Finally, show that the rules for addition and multiplication of real numbers hold also for complex numbers:

$$\frac{E_1}{A_1} + \frac{E_2}{A_2} = \frac{E_1 A_2 + E_2 A_1}{A_1 A_2} \quad \left(\text{Hint:} \frac{E_1}{A_1} = \frac{E_1 A_2}{A_1 A_2}\right)$$

$$\frac{E_1}{A_1} \cdot \frac{E_2}{A_2} = \frac{E_1 E_2}{A_1 A_2}.$$

In Case A is given in the form $A = a + bi$, we can find $1/A$ by multiplying the numerator and denominator of $1/(a + bi)$ by $a - bi$. (Compare the answer with Exercise 1 (d).)

As with real numbers, we define, for a negative integer $-n$, $A^{-n} = 1/A^n$.

2.2.6   COROLLARY   DeMoivre's Theorem

For every angle θ and every integer n, positive or negative,

$$(\cos\theta + i\sin\theta)^n = \cos n\theta + i\sin n\theta.$$

Problem 5. Give the proof. Then set $n = 3$ and derive formulas for $\cos 3\theta$ and $\sin 3\theta$ in terms of $\cos\theta$ and $\sin\theta$.

2.2.7   EXAMPLE

Find the complete solution, in the complex numbers, of $X^5 = 1$.

Solution. $X = 1$ is clearly a solution. Dividing $X^5 - 1$ by $X - 1$ we get the equation $X^4 + X^3 + X^2 + X + 1 = 0$ which cannot be factored in any obvious way. We try a geometric approach instead.

Write $X = |X|(\cos\theta + i\sin\theta)$. Then by Theorem 2.2.4 (used four times), the absolute value of X^5 is $|X|^5$. Since $X^5 = 1$, which has absolute value 1, we see that $|X|$ is a positive number such that $|X|^5 = 1$. In other words, $|X| = 1$.

Similarly, the polar angle 5θ of X^5 must equal the polar angle of 1. Hence

$$5\theta = 0° \text{ or } 360° \text{ or } 720° \text{ or } 1080° \text{ or } 1440° \text{ or} \ldots$$

so

$$\theta = 0° \text{ or } 72° \text{ or } 144° \text{ or } 216° \text{ or } 288° \text{ or} \ldots$$

Thus we have at least five solutions: $X = \cos 0 + i\sin 0 (= 1)$, $\cos 72° + i\sin 72°$, $\cos 144° + i\sin 144°$ and two others, similarly formed. Since an equation of degree 5 cannot have more than five solutions we have found all the solutions. (Thus, if continued indefinitely, the table of values of θ must repeat previously found solutions. To check this, note that the next entry would be $\theta = 1800/5 = 360°$, giving the same angle as $\theta = 0°$.)

Note that the difference of successive values of θ is always 72°. Thus the *five fifth roots of* 1 *are evenly spaced points on the circumference of the unit circle*, as shown in Figure 2.4. A similar statement holds for all six sixth roots of 1, all seven seventh roots, etc.

Problem 6. Find all six sixth roots of 1 by geometry. Check your answer by factoring $X^6 - 1 = (X^3 - 1)(X^3 + 1) = \cdots$.

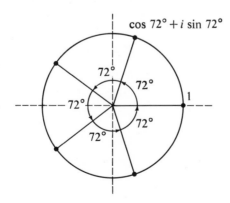

FIGURE 2.4

Problem 7. Find both square roots of i. Check your answer by squaring.

Problem 8. *Graphical representation of complex roots of quadratic equations.* Let $Z = X^2 - 6X + 13$.

(a) Find all values of X for which Z is a *real* number. (*Hint.* Let $X = x + yi$, x and y real. The set of all these numbers X will form a pair of perpendicular lines in the plane.)

(b) Choose a rectangular coordinate system in 3-dimensional space, such as that shown in Figure 2.5. Then, with each solution X of (a) we can associate the point (x, y, z) where $X = x + yi$ and $z =$ the *real* number $(x + iy)^2 - 6(x + iy) + 13$. Draw the graph of all these points (x, y, z).

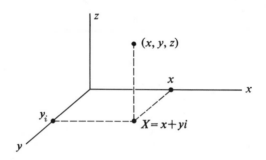

FIGURE 2.5

(*Answer.* The answer to part (b) will be a pair of parabolas perpendicular to each other. One of them will fail to meet the xy-plane, while the other will meet it at $3 + 2i$ and $3 - 2i$, the two roots of $X^2 - 6X + 13 = 0$.)

In closing, we recall that the complex numbers were constructed by enlarging the real numbers to contain a square root i of -1. Problem 7 shows that we don't have to make any further enlargement to get a square root of i. Example 2.2.7 and Problem 6 show further instances of the fact that the complex numbers contain more than merely solutions of $X^2 = -1$. These are all special cases of a famous theorem of Gauss, sometimes called the "Fundamental Theorem of Algebra": *Every equation*

$$A_n X^n + A_{n-1} X^{n-1} + A_{n-2} X^{n-2} + \cdots + A_1 X + A_0 = 0 \quad (A_n \neq 0)$$

of degree $n \geq 1$ (each A_j a complex number) has at least one solution in the complex numbers.

Thus the chain of successive enlargements of number systems—which began with the integers and successively made more algebraic equations solvable—comes to an end with the complex numbers. Unfortunately, Gauss's theorem is too hard to prove right now. But it will be proved in Chapter 6.

3 Similarities of the Plane

3.1   BASIC DEFINITIONS

DEFINITION

A *similarity* of the plane is a one-to-one function f: (the plane) onto (the plane) for which there is a positive real number m (called its *magnification ratio*) such that, for all points P and Q in the plane,

$$\text{dist}(P^f, Q^f) = m \, \text{dist}(P, Q).$$

Note that an isometry is a similarity whose magnification ratio is 1. To see the reason for the choice of terminology, let P, Q, R be the vertices of a triangle. Then

$$m = \frac{\text{dist}(P^f, Q^f)}{\text{dist}(P, Q)} = \frac{\text{dist}(P^f, R^f)}{\text{dist}(P, R)} = \frac{\text{dist}(Q^f, R^f)}{\text{dist}(Q, R)}$$

so that triangle PQR is similar to triangle $P^f Q^f R^f$ (Figure 3.1). The ratio by which each side of triangle PQR must be magnified to become as long as the corresponding side of triangle $P^f Q^f R^f$ is the magnification ratio m of f. Observe, however, that we allow magnification ratios $m \leq 1$, which is in slight conflict with the everyday meaning of the word "magnification".

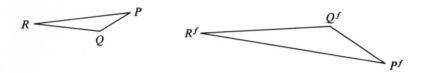

FIGURE 3.1

3.1.1   REMARK

Let f and g be similarities with magnification ratios m and n respectively. Then $f \circ g$ is a similarity and its magnification ratio is mn; f^{-1} is also a similarity and its magnification ratio is $1/m$. To establish the first assertion, choose points P and Q. Then

$$\text{dist}(P^{f \circ g}, Q^{f \circ g}) = n \, \text{dist}(P^f, Q^f) \quad \text{(since } g \text{ is a similarity)}$$
$$= nm \, \text{dist}(P, Q).$$

For the second assertion, recall (Remarks 1.4.3) that $X^{f^{-1}}$ is defined by

$$X^{f^{-1}} = \text{that point } P \text{ such that } P^f = X.$$

Exercise. Complete the proof of 3.1.1.

3.1.2   EXAMPLES AND NOTATION

Let A be a point and m a positive number. We define the *stretch* function $A(m)$ by: $P^{A(m)}$ is the point on ray $\overrightarrow{AP}$, such that $\text{dist}(A, P^{A(m)}) = m \, \text{dist}(A, P)$. Figure 3.2 illustrates what happens to two points P and Q when $m = 3$. For $m = \frac{1}{3}$ the diagram is as shown in Figure 3.3. The stretch $A(m)$ is also known

FIGURE 3.2

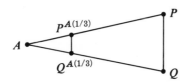

FIGURE 3.3

by the names *dilatation, dilation,* and *homothety.* We will call A the *center* of the stretch $A(m)$. To see that $A(m)$ is a similarity we first note that it is a one-to-one function: (the plane) onto (the plane). Then we observe that triangle APQ is similar to triangle $AP^{A(m)}Q^{A(m)}$ (see Figure 3.2 or 3.3) because the two triangles share an angle at A, and [by definition of $A(m)$] corresponding sides on each side of angle A are proportional

$$\frac{AP^{A(m)}}{AP} = m = \frac{AQ^{A(m)}}{AQ}.$$

Therefore the third pair of corresponding sides have the same ratio: $P^{A(m)}Q^{A(m)}/PQ = m$; that is, $\mathrm{dist}(P^{A(m)}, Q^{A(m)}) = m\,\mathrm{dist}(P, Q)$, as desired. We have also shown that *the ratio of magnification of $A(m)$ is m.*

A slightly more complex similarity is the *stretch rotation* $A(m, \theta)$ $= \mathrm{rot}(A, \theta) \circ A(m)$. (This also equals $A(m) \circ \mathrm{rot}(A, \theta)$). By 3.1.1, $A(m, \theta)$ is a similarity whose magnification ratio is m. When $\theta = 0$ we get $A(m, \theta)$ $= A(m)$; and when $m = 1$, $A(1, \theta) = \mathrm{rot}(A, \theta)$.

One other special case: The stretch $A(m)$ followed by reflection in point A ($m = \frac{1}{2}$ in Figure 3.4) is sometimes called a *negative stretch* and

FIGURE 3.4

written $A(-m)$. It can also be written $A(m, 180°)$. When the notation $A(-m)$ is used, it is important to realize that (when $m > 0$) the magnification ratio of $A(-m)$ is $+m$.

Other examples of similarities can be obtained by composing a stretch with a translation or with a reflection, and by composing any of the above similarities with any other. One special combination will be given a name: A *stretch reflection* is the composition of a reflection in a line and a stretch centered *at a point of the line*. The order in which the composition is performed is irrelevant because:

Problem 1. Let m be a positive number $\neq 1$, λ a line, and A a point. Show that

$$\text{refl}(\lambda) \circ A(m) = A(m) \circ \text{refl}(\lambda) \Leftrightarrow A \text{ is a point of } \lambda.$$

Problem 2. Let λ be a line and define a function g: (the plane) → (the plane) as follows. For a point P not on λ let A be the foot of the perpendicular from P to λ, and then let P^g be the point on ray $\overrightarrow{PA}$ such that $\text{dist}(A, P^g) = 2\,\text{dist}(P, A)$ (see Figure 3.5). For Q on λ let $Q^g = Q$. Is g a similarity? If so, what is its magnification ratio?

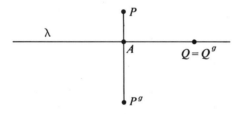

FIGURE 3.5

Problem 3. Let γ be a circle with center G and radius of length r; let A be a point outside the disk bounded by γ and m a positive number > 1. Show that as point P traces γ, $P^{A(m)}$ traces the circle γ' whose center is $G^{A(m)}$ and whose radius has length mr (Figure 3.6).

Problem 4. As in Problem 3, let A be a point outside the disk bounded by a circle γ with center G and radius r. Also, let γ' be the circle with center $G^{A(m)}$ (m a given positive number > 1) and radius mr (Figure 3.7). Show that there is a point B on line segment $GG^{A(m)}$ such that: As point

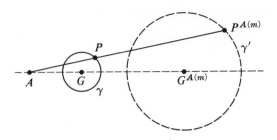

FIGURE 3.6

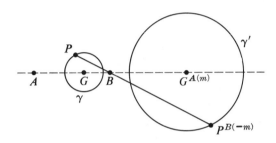

FIGURE 3.7

P traces circle γ, $P^{B(-m)}$ traces γ'. (The points A and B are sometimes called the *centers of similitude* of γ and γ'.)

Problem 5. Let λ be a straight line and f a similarity. Show that as point P traces λ, the path λ^f of P^f is again a straight line. (*Hint.* A point P belongs to line segment AB if and only if $\text{dist}(A, P) + \text{dist}(P, B) = \text{dist}(A, B)$.)

Problem 6. Let A, B, C, D be distinct points which lie on a circle, and let f be any similarity. Show that A^f, B^f, C^f, and D^f lie on a circle.

3.2   THE CLASSIFICATION THEOREM

The main problem of this chapter is to *describe all similarities of the plane, in a way that will make them easy to visualize.* The answer will appear in

Theorem 3.2.11, and our approach will be in three stages. We first show the relevance of the theorems on isometries proved in Chapter 1; then we show the relevance of the geometry of the complex numbers developed in Chapter 2; and finally we combine these ingredients to obtain the main theorem.

3.2.1   PROPOSITION

Let f and g be similarities of the plane which have the same effect on some three non-collinear points. Then $f = g$.

Proof. Let A, B, and C be the three given non-collinear points. Recall that g^{-1} and hence $f \circ g^{-1}$ is a similarity (Remark 3.1.1). Let p be the ratio of magnification of $f \circ g^{-1}$.

Apply g^{-1} to both sides of $A^f = A^g$, getting $A^{f \circ g^{-1}} = A^{g \circ g^{-1}} = A$. Similarly B and C are fixed points of $f \circ g^{-1}$.

$$\text{dist}(A, B) = \text{dist}(A^{f \circ g^{-1}}, B^{f \circ g^{-1}}) \quad (\text{since } A^{f \circ g^{-1}} = A \text{ and } B^{f \circ g^{-1}} = B)$$
$$= p \, \text{dist}(A, B) \quad (\text{definition of "similarity"}).$$

Since $A \neq B$, and hence $\text{dist}(A, B) \neq 0$, we conclude that $p = 1$. In other words, $f \circ g^{-1}$ is an *isometry* with three non-collinear fixed points. Therefore (Proposition 1.4.1) $f \circ g^{-1} = \text{id}$, the identity function. Composing this equation with g on the right we get $f = g$ as desired.   □

3.2.2   PROPOSITION

Let f be a similarity with ratio of magnification m, and let A be any point. Then, for some isometry g, there is a factorization $f = g \circ A(m)$.

Proof. Let $g = f \circ A(1/m)$. Then g, being a composition of similarities is itself a similarity and its ratio of magnification is $m(1/m) = 1$ (Remark 3.1.1); in other words, g is an isometry. Composing $g = f \circ A(1/m)$ on the right with $A(m)$ we get $g \circ A(m) = f$ as desired.   □

3.2.3   COROLLARY

Every similarity must be either direct or opposite.

Proof. Write f in the form $f = g \circ A(m)$ (A being *any* point.) Since $A(m)$ is clearly a direct function and the isometry g must be either direct or opposite (Remark 1.4.10), it follows that f must be direct or opposite. □

We now investigate the relevance of the complex numbers to our problem. Let $A = (\frac{1}{4}) + i(\sqrt{\frac{3}{4}})$. In polar form $A = (\frac{1}{2})(\cos 60° + i \sin 60°)$. Then for an arbitrary complex number X we can find the point ($=$ complex number) $A \cdot X$ (the dot indicates multiplication) by multiplying the absolute value of X by $\frac{1}{2}$ and adding $60°$ to the polar angle of X (Theorem 2.2.4) (see Figure 3.8). In other words, the function $X \to A \cdot X$ is a stretch rotation: $A \cdot X = X^{0\,(1/2,\,60°)}$. This is a special case of the following lemma.

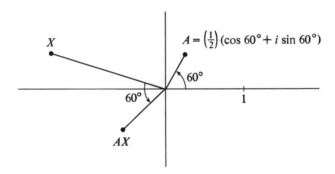

FIGURE 3.8

3.2.4   LEMMA

For all complex numbers B, C, X, positive numbers m, and angles θ:

(i) $X^{\text{trans } \vec{0B}} = X + B$, and $X^{\vec{B0}} = X - B$

(ii) $X^{0\,(m,\theta)} = m(\cos\theta + i\sin\theta)X$

(iii) $X^{C\,(m,\theta)} = m(\cos\theta + i\sin\theta)(X - C) + C$.

Proof. Assertions (i) and (ii) are merely restatements of Theorems 2.2.1 and 2.2.4 in language more useful to this chapter. In order to obtain (iii) it will be sufficient to prove

(1) $C(m, \theta) = (\text{trans } \vec{C0}) \circ 0(m, \theta) \circ \text{trans } \vec{0C}$

for then, writing A for $m(\cos\theta + i\sin\theta)$, we get,

$$X^{C(m,\,\theta)} = X^{(\text{trans } \vec{C0})\,\circ\,0(m,\,\theta)\,\circ\,\text{trans }\vec{0C}}$$

$$= (X - C)^{0\,(m,\,\theta)\,\circ\,\text{trans }\vec{0C}} \qquad (\text{by (i)})$$

$$= [A(X - C)]^{\text{trans }\vec{0C}} \qquad (\text{by (ii)})$$

$$= A(X - C) + C$$

as desired.   ☐

Problem 1. Prove equation (1) above. (*Hint.* Show first that

$(\text{trans } \vec{C0})\circ 0(m,\,\theta)\circ(\text{trans }\vec{0C})\circ C(1/m)$ is a direct isometry with C as a fixed point.)

Exercise. Let $X^f = (1 + i)X + 3$.

(a) Write $1 + i$ in polar form $m(\cos\theta + i\sin\theta)$ and then use (i) and (ii) of the lemma to interpret f as a stretch rotation followed by a translation.

(b) Find a complex number C such that f can be written in the form

$$X^f = m(\cos\theta + i\sin\theta)(X - C) + C$$

with the same m and θ as in part (a). Then use (iii) of the lemma to interpret f as a stretch rotation.

(c) Compute $(1 - i)^f$ and compare the answer with that obtained by applying the geometric interpretations (a) and (b) to $(1 - i)$.

3.2.5   LEMMA

Let A and B be complex numbers with $A \neq 0$ and let the function f: (the plane) → (the plane) be defined by $X^f = AX + B$. Also let the polar form of A be $m(\cos\theta + i\sin\theta)$. Then

(i) (If $A = 1$) $f = \text{trans } \vec{0B}$.

(ii) (If $A \neq 1$) $f = C(m,\,\theta)$ where $C = B/(1 - A)$.

Proof. (i) is part of 3.2.4. To obtain (ii) we try to find a complex number C such that

$$AX + B = A(X - C) + C \qquad \text{for all } X.$$

This will hold if the constant term on the left-hand side equals the constant term on the right-hand side. That is, if $B = -AC + C = (-A + 1)C$. Since $A \neq 1$, $C = B/(1 - A)$ will do. Then Lemma 3.2.4 (iii) proves (ii) of the present lemma. ☐

Problem 2. (a) Let θ be the acute angle whose cosine equals $\frac{3}{5}$ ($\theta =$ approximately 53°). Write $X^{0(5, \theta)}$ and $X^{H(1/2)}$ (where $H = 1 + 4i$) in the form $AX + B$. Then write $X^{0(5, \theta) \circ H(1/2)}$ in this form and use this to express the composition $0(5, \theta) \circ H(\frac{1}{2})$ as a single stretch rotation. (*Answer.* $0(5, \theta) \circ H(\frac{1}{2}) = K(\frac{5}{2}, \theta)$ where $K = -1$.)

(b) Verify the above composition approximately on graph paper for some particular point X.

Problem 3. Write the formulas for $X^{H(2, 30°)}$ ($H = 1 + i$) and $X^{0(1/2, -30°)}$, then the formula for $X^{H(2, 30°) \circ 0(1/2, -30°)}$. Give a simple geometric description of the similarity $H(2, 30°) \circ 0(\frac{1}{2}, -30°)$. (*Hint.* It will be a translation or rotation.) Then check each portion of your answer approximately on graph paper.

Problem 4. Let θ and K be as in Problem 2. Are there points $L \neq 0$ and M such that $(\text{trans } \overrightarrow{0L}) \circ M(\frac{5}{2}, \theta) = K(\frac{5}{2}, \theta)$? (If "no" give a proof. If "yes" find them.)

We have now assembled enough information to describe all direct similarities.

3.2.6   PROPOSITION

Every direct similarity is either a translation or a stretch rotation.

Proof. Let f be the given direct similarity. By Proposition 3.2.2 there is a factorization $f = g \circ 0(m)$ where g is an isometry. Since $0(m)$ is a direct similarity, g must also be direct [otherwise $f = (\text{opposite}) \circ (\text{direct}) = $ opposite]. Hence by the classification theorem for isometries (1.4.8), g must be a translation or a rotation.

In either case there is a formula

(1) $$X^g = A_1 X + B_1 \qquad (A_1 \neq 0)$$

for if $g = \text{trans } \overrightarrow{OB_1}$, then, by Lemma 3.2.4, $X^g = X + B_1$; and if $g = \text{rot}(C, \theta)$ $= C(1, \theta)$, 3.2.4 again shows that $X^g = A_1 X + (-A_1 C + C)$ where $A_1 =$ $= \cos \theta + i \sin \theta$. Therefore:

$$(2) \quad X^f = X^{g \circ 0(m)} = X^{g \circ 0(m, \, 0°)}$$
$$= (A_1 X + B_1)^{0(m, \, 0°)} \qquad \text{(by (1))}$$
$$= A_2 (A_1 X + B_1) \qquad \text{(by 3.2.4 (ii)) with } A_2 = m(\cos 0 + i \sin 0)$$
$$= (A_2 A_1) X + (A_2 B_1)$$

so that, by Lemma 3.2.5, f must be a translation or a stretch rotation; and this completes the proof. $\square$

From equation (2) above we obtain a converse to Lemma 3.2.5 which we will need soon.

3.2.7   COROLLARY

For every direct similarity f there exist complex numbers $A \, (\neq 0)$ and B such that

$$X^f = AX + B \qquad \text{for all complex numbers } X.$$

Another, more geometric proof of Proposition 3.2.6 can be given for the case where f is known in advance to have a fixed point. This is suggested by:

Problem 5. Let f be a direct similarity with magnification ratio m and with at least one fixed point F. Show that, for any points A and X, non-collinear with F, triangle FAX is similar to triangle FA^fX^f. Use this to conclude that $f = F(m, \theta)$ for some m (see Figure 3.9). Note that when

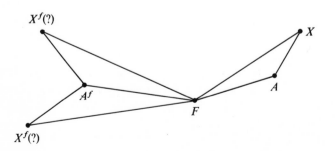

FIGURE 3.9

X is *on* line FA, this proof will break down. But then 3.2.1 will help.

In order to deal with opposite similarities we introduce another operation in the complex numbers. The *complex conjugate* of $A = x + yi$ (x, y real) is defined to be the complex number $\bar{A} = x - yi$.

3.2.8   REMARKS

(i) The reflection of $A = x + yi$ (x, y real) in the real axis is the point $\bar{A}$, as Figure 3.10 indicates.

(ii) The following formulas hold for all complex numbers A and B.

If $A = m(\cos\theta + i\sin\theta)$ $(m > 0)$ then $\bar{A} = m(\cos(-\theta) + i\sin(-\theta))$

$$\overline{A + B} = \bar{A} + \bar{B}$$
$$\overline{A \cdot B} \;\; = \bar{A} \cdot \bar{B}$$
$$\overline{A/B} \;\; = \bar{A}/\bar{B}$$
$$\text{If } |A| \;\; = 1, \text{ then } \bar{A} = 1/A$$
$$A \cdot \bar{A} \;\; = |A|^2 .$$

Exercise. Verify the above formulas.

(iii) For every opposite similarity f there exist complex numbers $A(\neq 0)$ and B such that

$$X^f = A\bar{X} + B \text{ for all complex numbers } X .$$

$|A|$ is then the magnification ratio of f.

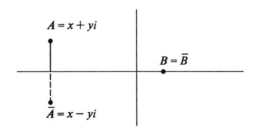

FIGURE 3.10

To prove (iii), let r be reflection in the real axis. Then, since f and r are both opposite similarities, $r \circ f$ is a direct similarity and hence it has a formula $X^{r \circ f} = AX + B$ for suitable $A (\neq 0)$ and B (by Corollary 3.2.7). Then

$$X^f = X^{r \circ r \circ f} = \bar{X}^{r \circ f} = A\bar{X} + B.$$

Exercise. Show that $|A| = $ magnification ratio of f. □

Exercise. Prove the converse of (iii) above; that is, *if f is defined by $X^f = A\bar{X} + B (A \neq 0)$, then f is an opposite similarity with magnification ratio $|A|$.* (*Hint.* Compose f with $r = $ reflection in the real axis.)

The following lemma, while not very interesting in its own right will occur as one of the computations in the proof of the Classification Theorem. Since the lemma's proof is messy, it would make the main ideas of the proof of the theorem harder to understand if done in the body of that proof. Hence we prove it separately.

3.2.9   LEMMA

Let A and B be complex numbers such that the equation $A\bar{X} + B = X$ has *no* solution X. Then $|A| = 1$.

Proof. Note that the lemma does not claim that if $|A| = 1$ the equation has no solution. It merely states that the equation is always solvable *except possibly if $|A| = 1$.*

Write $A = a + bi$, $B = c + di$, $X = x + yi$ (a, b, c, d, x, y real), so that the given equation becomes

$$(a + bi)(x - yi) + (c + di) = x + yi.$$

"Multiplying out" the parentheses and then collecting real and imaginary parts, we get

$$(ax + by + c) + (bx - ay + d)i = x + yi.$$

Therefore the original equation is the same as the *pair* of simultaneous equations

$$\begin{cases} ax + by + c = x & (= \text{the real part of each side}) \\ bx - ay + d = y & (= \text{the imaginary part of each side}). \end{cases}$$

These can be rewritten:

(1)
$$\begin{cases} (1-a)\,x - by = c \\ -bx + (1+a)\,y = d. \end{cases}$$

This can always be solved for x and y using the determinant formula, provided that the determinant which occurs in the denominator is not zero. Hence the hypothesis that *no* solution exists asserts that

$$0 = \det \begin{vmatrix} 1-a & -b \\ -b & 1+a \end{vmatrix} = 1 - a^2 - b^2.$$

In other words, $1 = a^2 + b^2 = |A|^2$. Since $|A| \geq 0$ we conclude $1 = |A|$. ☐

Readers not familiar with the solution of (1) by determinants will also find, after attempting to solve (1) by some other method, that a solution can always be found except (possibly) if $a^2 + b^2 = 1$.

Recall that a *stretch reflection* is the composition of reflection in a line and a stretch centered at a point of that line.

3.2.10   PROPOSITION

Every opposite similarity is either a glide reflection or a stretch reflection.

Proof.   Let f be the given opposite similarity. We consider two cases.

Case 1. f has at least one fixed point. We can choose a coordinate system such that this fixed point is the origin. By Remarks 3.2.8 (iii), f has a formula $X^f = A\bar{X} + B$ with $|A| = m$ the magnification ratio of f. Since $0^f = 0$, setting $X = 0$ in this formula gives $0 = 0 + B$. Thus

(1) $X^f = A\bar{X}$ for all X.

If we write $A = m(\cos\theta + i\sin\theta)$ and let $r = $ reflection in the real axis we see (Lemma 3.2.4) that

(2) $f = r \circ 0(m, \theta) = r \circ \mathrm{rot}(0, \theta) \circ 0(m).$

We can simplify (2) as follows. Let λ be the line such that the directed angle from the positive real axis to λ equals $\theta/2$. Then (Corollary 1.4.5) $\mathrm{rot}(0, \theta) = $ $= r \circ \mathrm{refl}(\lambda)$. Substituting this into (2) we obtain (Figure 3.11)

$$f = r \circ r \circ \mathrm{refl}(\lambda) \circ 0(m) = \mathrm{refl}(\lambda) \circ 0(m).$$

Hence f is a stretch reflection, as desired.

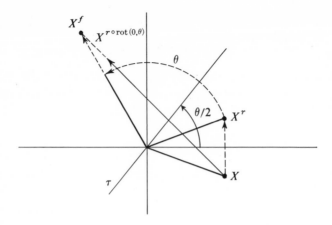

FIGURE 3.11

Case 2. f has no fixed points. This time choose *any* coordinate system. Again, by 3.2.8 (iii), f has a formula $X^f = A\bar{X} + B$ with $|A|$ the magnification ratio of f. The hypothesis of Case 2 is that no point X satisfies $X = X^f$, that is, the equation

$$X = A\bar{X} + B \qquad \text{has no solution } X.$$

Lemma 3.2.9 then shows that $|A| = 1$; in other words f is an opposite *isometry*. Finally the classification theorem for isometries (1.4.8) shows that f is a glide reflection. ☐

We summarize 3.2.3, the above proposition, and 3.2.6 in this theorem:

3.2.11   CLASSIFICATION THEOREM FOR SIMILARITIES

Every similarity of the plane must be either
  (i) (If direct) a translation or a stretch rotation; or
  (ii) (If opposite) a glide reflection or a stretch reflection.

Problem 6. Find all similarities f such that $0^f = 4i$ and $1^f = 2i$, and express them in the form (i) and (ii) of the classification theorem, giving numerical values for C, m, and θ if $f = C(m, \theta)$ etc. (*Hints.* A line of reflection can be specified by giving 2 points on it. Any direct f will have a formula $X^f = AX + B$.)

Problem 7*. Let A, B, C, D be points with $A \neq B$ and $C \neq D$. Show that there are exactly two similarities f of the plane, one direct, and one opposite, such that $A^f = C$ and $B^f = D$.

Problem 8*. Let A, B, and X be complex numbers with $A \neq B$. Find, in terms of complex arithmetic, the reflection X^r of X in the line joining A and B. (*Hint.* One form which the answer can take is

$$X^r = \frac{A - B}{\bar{A} - \bar{B}} (\bar{X} - \bar{B}) + B.)$$

Problem 9. Let θ and φ be directed angles and C, D be points with $C \neq D$. Using the complex numbers express the composition $\mathrm{rot}(C, \theta) \circ \mathrm{rot}(D, \varphi)$ as a single translation, rotation, or glide reflection. (Compare with the solution of Problem 8, p. 31.)

Problem 10. Let A and B be complex numbers with $0 \neq |A| \neq 1$, and let the function $f:$ (the plane) $\rightarrow$ (the plane) be defined by $X^f = A\bar{X} + B$. Prove that f is a stretch reflection, find the coordinates of its center, the ratio of stretch, and the line of reflection. (*Hint* for finding the fixed point F. $F = A\bar{F} + B$, hence also $\bar{F} = \bar{A}F + \bar{B}$. Substitute the second equation into the first.)

Problem 11*. Find all similarities f of the plane such that for every pair of distinct points A and B, line AB is parallel to line $A^f B^f$.

Problem 12. Let A and B be given points. Express $A(3) \circ B(\tfrac{1}{3})$ in simplest form.

Problem 13. The same as Problem 6 with $0^f = \sqrt{3} + i$ and $1^f = 0$.

3.3   CIRCLE- AND LINE-PRESERVING FUNCTIONS

Which $1 - 1$ functions: (the plane) $\rightarrow$ (the plane) preserve the shapes of geometric figures? That is, which have the property that for every geometric figure $\mathscr{P}$, $\mathscr{P}^f$ has the "same shape" as $\mathscr{P}$? Isometries have this property, as one can tell from a glance at the classification theorem. If we consider a triangle to have the same shape as every triangle *similar* to it (although the triangles might have different sizes) then all similarities will preserve the shapes of triangles. In order to find all shape-preserving functions we must say, first, exactly what we mean by "shape of a geometric figure". While there may be a certain amount of difference of opinion from person to person about this, the following two properties of a function f will probably be a part of anybody's definition:

> (CP) For every circle γ, γ^f is again a circle; and
> (LP) For every straight line λ, λ^f is again a straight line.

To see that similarities always have these properties, let m be the magnification ratio of f, G the center and r the radius of γ. Then, "P is a point of γ", means that $\text{dist}(P, G) = r$;† and this is true if and only if $\text{dist}(P^f, G^f) = mr$, which is equivalent to, "P^f is a point of the circle of radius mr centered at G^f". Property (LP) was Problem 5, p. 67 (alternatively, it can be proved by observing that stretches are line-preserving, and then applying the classification theorem for similarities).

Notation.   Throughout this section f will be any $1 - 1$ function: (the plane) $\rightarrow$ (the plane) such that (CP) and (LP) hold. Our problem in this section will be: *Find all such functions f*. The answer will be that every such f must be a similarity (Theorem 3.3.10). We therefore won't have to worry about what else should have gone into the definition of "shape of a geometric figure".

Note that we have *not* assumed that f preserves betweenness; that is, if point B is between A and C on line λ, we have not assumed that B^f is between A^f and C^f on λ^f. We have also not assumed that f is onto; nor do we know if $\text{dist}(A, B)$ is related in any way to $\text{dist}(A^f, B^f)$.

Much of the solution of the above problem will be given as problems with hints. We begin with a lemma.

3.3.1   LEMMA

(i) If lines λ and μ are parallel, then so are lines λ^f and μ^f.

(ii) If line λ is tangent to circle γ at A, then line λ^f is tangent to circle γ^f at A^f.

Proof.   Since f is $1 - 1$, the number of points of intersection of any sets of points λ and μ is the same as the number of points of intersection of λ^f and μ^f. If the intersection of λ and μ consists of exactly one point A, then A^f

---

† Note that we are using "circle" to denote points on the circumference of a circle. The set of points P such that $\text{dist}(P, G) \leq r$ will be called a *disk*.

is a point of the intersection of λ^f and μ^f, hence is the unique point of this intersection. This proves (ii); (i) is proved similarly. ⬚

3.3.2   LEMMA

(i) If A and B are endpoints of a diameter of a circle γ, then A^f and B^f are endpoints of a diameter of γ^f.

(ii) If G is the center of a circle γ, then G^f is the center of γ^f.

Proof.   Since we don't know what f does to distances, we have to redefine "diameter" and "center" in terms of properties f is known to preserve.

Let λ be the line containing a given diameter AB of γ, and let μ and v be the lines tangent to γ at A and B respectively. Then μ is parallel to v

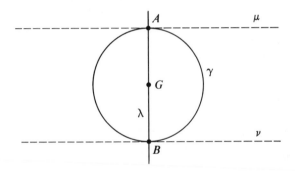

FIGURE 3.12

because both are perpendicular to λ ("a tangent to a circle and the radius to the point of tangency are perpendicular".) By Lemma 3.3.1, μ^f and v^f will be parallel to each other and tangent to γ^f at A^f and B^f respectively. This forces A^f and B^f to be end-points of a diameter of γ^f, because of the following:

Exercise. (Prove that) If line segment HK is not a diameter of circle δ, then the tangents μ and v to δ at H and K respectively meet (see Figure 3.13).

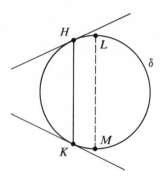

FIGURE 3.13

Thus we have established (i). To establish (ii) let λ_1 and λ_2 be any two lines through the center G of γ. Then $(\lambda_1)^f$ and $(\lambda_2)^f$ pass through the center of γ^f by (i), hence their intersection *is* the center of γ^f. But G^f is the intersection of $(\lambda_1)^f$ and $(\lambda_2)^f$; and this proves (ii).   ☐

3.3.3   LEMMA

If B is an interior point of the disk bounded by a circle γ, then B^f is an interior point of the disk bounded by γ^f.

Problem 1. Give the proof. (*Hint.* See Figure 3.14.)

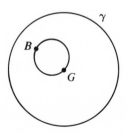

FIGURE 3.14

3.3.4   LEMMA

If point B is between A and C on line λ, then B^f is between A^f and C^f on λ^f.

Problem 2. Give a proof. (*Hint.* See Figure 3.15.)

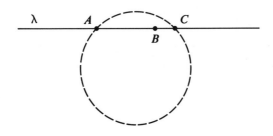

FIGURE 3.15

3.3.5   LEMMA

(i)   If σ is a line segment with endpoints A and C, then σ^f is a line segment with endpoints A^f and C^f.

(ii)   If line segment σ is a diameter of circle γ, then σ^f is a diameter of γ^f.

(iii)   If line λ is the perpendicular bisector of $\sigma =$ line segment AC, then λ^f is the perpendicular bisector of $\sigma^f =$ line segment A^fC^f.

Proof.   (i) is essentially a consequence of 3.3.4. But there is a subtlety too easily passed over: 3.3.4 says only that σ^f is *contained in* line segment A^fC^f. It still must be shown that every point U of segment A^fC^f has the form $U = B^f$ for some point B of segment AC.

So, suppose some point U does not have this form. Since U is a point of *line* $A^fC^f =$ (line AC)^f, U has the form $U = D^f$ for some point D of line AC, where D is not part of line *segment* AC. Hence either A is between C

FIGURE 3.16

and D or C is between A and D. In either case, applying 3.3.4 to points A, D, and C will yield the contradiction that $D^f = U$ is not between A^f and C^f. Hence our unproved supposition about U was wrong, and therefore U does have the required form.

(ii) is an immediate consequence of (i) and 3.2 (i), and (iii) is Problem 3 below. $\square$

Problem 3. Prove (iii). (*Hint.* See Figure 3.17.)

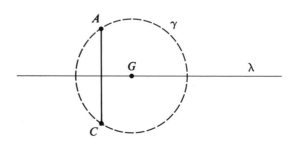

FIGURE 3.17

3.3.6   LEMMA

Let A, B, C, D be arbitrary points in the plane.
  (i) If $\operatorname{dist}(A, B) = \operatorname{dist}(C, D)$, then $\operatorname{dist}(A^f, B^f) = \operatorname{dist}(C^f, D^f)$.
  (ii) If $\operatorname{dist}(A, B) < \operatorname{dist}(C, D)$, then $\operatorname{dist}(A^f, B^f) < \operatorname{dist}(C^f, D^f)$.

Proof. (i) We consider 3 cases.

Case 1. $A = C$. We can assume $B \neq D$, for if $B = D$ *and* $A = C$, then clearly $\operatorname{dist}(A, B) = \operatorname{dist}(C, D)$. Our hypothesis is that triangle ABD is isosceles. Another way of saying this is that the perpendicular bisector λ of line segment BD passes through A (see Figure 3.18). Hence λ^f—which, by 3.3.5 (iii), is the perpendicular bisector of segment $B^f D^f$—passes through A^f, and this shows that $\operatorname{dist}(A^f, B^f) = \operatorname{dist}(A^f, D^f)$ as desired.

Case 2. A is not collinear with C and D. Then draw a parallelogram $ACDE$. By 3.3.1, line $A^f E^f$ is parallel to line $C^f D^f$, and line $A^f C^f$ is parallel to line $E^f D^f$. Hence A^f, C^f, D^f, E^f are consecutive vertices of a parallelo-

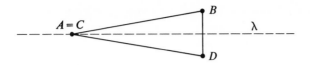

FIGURE 3.18

gram and its opposite sides $A^f E^f$ and $C^f D^f$ therefore have equal length. (*Note*. We have tacitly made use of the fact that f is $1 - 1$, for if it were not, line $C^f D^f$ might not be distinct from line $A^f E^f$ and we might not have a genuine parallelogram after applying f.) Since by Case 1, $\text{dist}(A^f, E^f) = \text{dist}(A^f, B^f)$, Case 2 is now proved (see Figure 3.19).

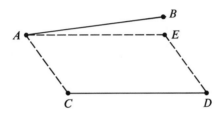

FIGURE 3.19

Case 3. A, C, and D are collinear, but $A \neq C$. Here pick any pair of points C' and D' such that C, D, D', C' are consecutive vertices of a parallelogram (see Figure 3.20) and then apply Case 2 twice.

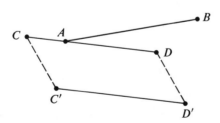

FIGURE 3.20

(ii) For the inequality, let E be the point on line segment CD such that $\text{dist}(C, E) = \text{dist}(A, B)$. By 3.3.4, E^f will be between C^f and D^f on line $C^f D^f$. Hence, by (i),

$$\text{dist}(A, B) = \text{dist}(C^f, E^f) < \text{dist}(C^f, D^f). \quad \square$$

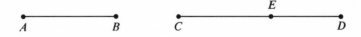

FIGURE 3.21

3.3.7   LEMMA

Let A, B, C, D be points and q a positive real number such that $\text{dist}(A, B) = q \cdot \text{dist}(C, D)$. Then $\text{dist}(A^f, B^f) = q \cdot \text{dist}(C^f, D^f)$.

Proof. We can suppose that $C \neq D$ (and hence $A \neq B$), because then the result is obvious. The case $q = 1$ was done in 3.3.6. For q a positive integer divide segment AB into q equal portions, each of length $\text{dist}(C, D)$, as in Figure 3.22. By 3.3.6, $\text{dist}(A_i^f, A_{i+1}^f) = \text{dist}(C^f, D^f)$ for each i. By repeated use of 3.3.4 the points $(A_i)^f$ have the order shown in Figure 3.23. Hence $\text{dist}(A^f, B^f) = q \cdot \text{dist}(C^f, D^f)$.

$$A = A_0 \quad A_1 \quad A_2 \quad A_3 \qquad\qquad\qquad A_{q-1} \quad A_q = B$$

FIGURE 3.22

FIGURE 3.23

Problem 4. Do the case that q is a positive rational number, that is, $q = m/n$ with m and n positive integers. (*Hint.* Clear of fractions to reduce to the previous case.)

For the general case (q any positive real number), let q_i be the approximation of q to i decimal places. (Do *not* "round off" the last digit.) Then q_i is a rational number, $q_i \leq q < q_i + 1/10^i$, and, in fact,

(1) q is the unique positive number x such that for *every* i,
$$q_i \leq x < q_i + 1/10^i.$$

(Statement (1) is, in fact, what we mean by the "decimal expansion" of a real number.) Using (1) we can draw Figure 3.24 (points E_i and F_i being defined by the distances indicated below them). Applying f to Figure 3.24, we get

$$
\begin{aligned}
q_i \operatorname{dist}(C^f, D^f) &= \operatorname{dist}(A^f, E_i^f) && \text{(the rational case of the lemma)} \\
&< \operatorname{dist}(A^f, B^f) && \text{(betweenness)} \\
&< \operatorname{dist}(A^f, F_i^f) \\
&= (q_i + 1/10^i) \operatorname{dist}(C^f, D^f).
\end{aligned}
$$

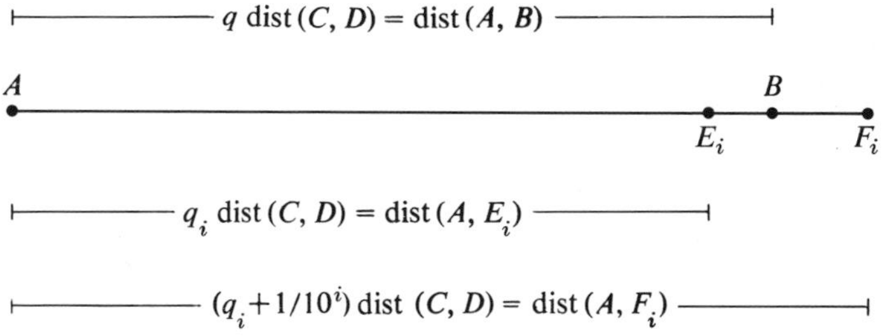

$$\vdash\!\!\!\!-\!\!\!\!-\!\!\!\!-\ q \operatorname{dist}(C, D) = \operatorname{dist}(A, B)\ -\!\!\!\!-\!\!\!\!-\!\!\!\!\dashv$$

A •——————————————————————————•B •
E_i F_i

$$\vdash\!\!\!\!-\!\!\!\!-\ q_i \operatorname{dist}(C, D) = \operatorname{dist}(A, E_i)\ -\!\!\!\!-\!\!\!\!\dashv$$

$$\vdash\!\!\!\!-\!\!\!\!-\ (q_i + 1/10^i) \operatorname{dist}(C, D) = \operatorname{dist}(A, F_i)\ -\!\!\!\!-\!\!\!\!\dashv$$

FIGURE 3.24

Dividing by $\operatorname{dist}(C^f, D^f)$ which can't be 0 since f is $1-1$, we get

$$
(2) \qquad\qquad q_i < \frac{\operatorname{dist}(A^f, B^f)}{\operatorname{dist}(C^f, D^f)} < (q_i + 1/10^i)
$$

for *every* i. Statement (1) now shows that the middle term of (2) equals q, and this completes the proof. □

Notation. Let A, B, C be distinct points and D, E, F be distinct points. We will use the notation "$\triangle$"$ABC \sim$ "$\triangle$"DEF to mean that either ABC and DEF are similar triangles with $A \leftrightarrow D$, $B \leftrightarrow E$, and $C \leftrightarrow F$ corresponding vertices, or else that both "triangles" are line segments with $\operatorname{dist}(A, B)/\operatorname{dist}(D, E) = \operatorname{dist}(A, C)/\operatorname{dist}(D, F) = \operatorname{dist}(B, C)/\operatorname{dist}(E, F)$ (see Figure 3.25).

This notation will save us the trouble of stating many special cases in what follows.

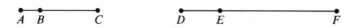

A B C D E F

FIGURE 3.25

3.3.8   PROPOSITION

If A, B, C are any 3 distinct points, then "$\triangle$"$ABC \sim$ "$\triangle$"$A^f B^f C^f$.

Proof. Let $\text{dist}(A, B) = q \cdot \text{dist}(A, C)$ and $\text{dist}(A, B) = r \cdot \text{dist}(B, C)$. Then, by 3.3.7,

$$\frac{\text{dist}(A, B)}{\text{dist}(A^f, B^f)} = \frac{q \cdot \text{dist}(A, C)}{q \cdot \text{dist}(A^f, C^f)} = \frac{r \cdot \text{dist}(B, C)}{r \cdot \text{dist}(B^f, C^f)}.$$

After cancelling q and r and using Problem 5 below, we get the desired conclusion. ▯

Problem 5. A, B, and C are collinear if and only if A^f, B^f, and C^f are collinear. (*Hint.* Use 3.3.7 again.)

3.3.9   PROPOSITION

f is onto.

Proof. Let U be any point of the plane. We have to show that $U = C^f$ for some C. Pick any two distinct points A and B. If $A^f = U$ or $B^f = U$ we're done. Otherwise draw "$\triangle$"$A^f B^f U$ (Figure 3.26) and then choose distinct

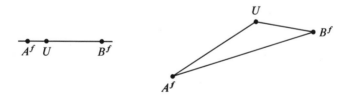

FIGURE 3.26

points C and D (exception: $C = D$ if A^f, B^f and U are collinear) such that "$\triangle$"$ABC \sim$ "$\triangle$"$A^f B^f U$ and "$\triangle$"$ABD \sim$ "$\triangle$"$A^f B^f U$. Applying f to Figure 3.27 and using 3.3.8 we see that either $C^f = U$ or $D^f = U$. (Again we have tacitly used the fact that f is $1 - 1$, because we need $C^f \neq D^f$ in order to conclude that one of these must equal U.) ▯

With all of this preparatory work done, we now obtain the answer to our problem. Note what still has to be done. We have to show that the ratio of similarity given by 3.3.8 is the same for every three points A, B, and C.

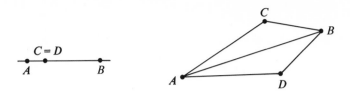

FIGURE 3.27

3.3.10   THEOREM

Every $1-1$ function f: (the plane) $\rightarrow$ (the plane) which takes circles to circles and lines to lines must be a similarity.

Proof.   Choose a pair of distinct points A and B (these will be kept fixed) and choose the unit of length so that $\text{dist}(A, B) = 1$. Then let $m = \text{dist}(A^f, B^f)$. We show that f is a similarity with magnification ratio m; that is,

$$(1) \qquad \text{dist}(P^f, Q^f) = m\,\text{dist}(P, Q)$$

for every choice of P and Q. By 3.3.8, "$\triangle$"$ABQ \sim$ "$\triangle$"$A^f B^f Q^f$, so

$$(2) \qquad \frac{\text{dist}(A, Q)}{\text{dist}(A^f, Q^f)} = \frac{1}{m}.$$

Also "$\triangle$"$PAQ \sim$ "$\triangle$"$P^f A^f Q^f$, so

$$\frac{\text{dist}(P, Q)}{\text{dist}(P^f, Q^f)} = \frac{\text{dist}(A, Q)}{\text{dist}(A^f, Q^f)}$$

$$= \frac{1}{m} \qquad \left(\text{by (2)}\right)$$

and this completes the proof. (*Note.* We have tacitly assumed that points A, B, Q are distinct and also points P, A, Q are distinct. If not, it is easy to deal with these cases individually.) □

Problem 6*. Let f be a function: (the real numbers) $\rightarrow$ (the real numbers) such that $f(x+y) = f(x) + f(y)$ for all x and y.

(a) Show that, for every *rational* number x, $f(x) = cx$ where $c = f(1)$. (*Hint.* First prove it for every *integer* x.)

(b) Given the additional hypothesis that, for every two real numbers $x < y$, the inequality $f(x) < f(y)$ must also hold, prove that $f(x) = cx$ for every real number x (c still equals $f(1)$). (*Hint.* See the proof of 3.3.7.)

---

4 Circular Inversion

4.1　INTRODUCTION

This chapter deals with a geometric function "inversion in a circle" which, unlike isometry and similarity, preserves neither the size nor the shape of geometric figures. What properties of geometric interest such a function can have provide the central theme of this chapter.

First of all, we define and make some simple observations about inversion. In Section 4.2 we see what inversion does to circles, lines, and angles. In Section 4.3 we make use of the way in which inversion changes shapes to prove some theorems about circles and lines. Finally, in the last section, we connect inversion with isometry and similarity.

DEFINITIONS

Let γ be a circle with center G and radius of length g, or, in brief, let $\gamma = $ circle (G, g). For a point $H \neq G$, we define $H^{\text{inv}\,\gamma}$ (the *inverse* of H in γ) to be that point on ray $\overrightarrow{GH}$ (that is, on line segment GH extended through H) such that

(1) $$\text{dist}(G, H) \cdot \text{dist}(G, H^{\text{inv}\,\gamma}) = g^2.$$

We have not defined $G^{\text{inv}\,\gamma}$ because the equation $0 \cdot d = g^2$ has no solution d.

The point G is sometimes called the *center of inversion*, and γ is called the *circle of inversion*.

Figure 4.1 shows $\gamma = $ circle $(G, 6)$. Note that $H^{\text{inv}\,\gamma} = K$ and also that $K^{\text{inv}\,\gamma} = H$.

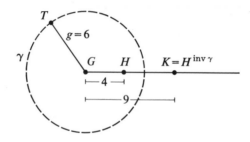

FIGURE 4.1

A moment of thought will show that, if γ is any circle,

$$H^{\text{inv}\,\gamma} = K \iff H = K^{\text{inv}\,\gamma}.$$

When we wish to call attention to this symmetry we will speak of two points H and K being *mutually inverse* in γ.

Another fact illustrated in Figure 4.1 is that if $H(\neq G)$ is interior to the disk bounded by γ, then K is exterior to that disk. That this is always true can be seen by referring to equation (1) and observing that if the product of two positive numbers equals g^2 and one of them is $< g$, then the other must be $> g$. Thus, inv γ is a $1 - 1$ *function: (the plane punctured at G) onto (the plane punctured at G) which interchanges the interior and the exterior of the disk bounded by γ. Its fixed points are precisely the points of γ itself.*

The reason for the choice of terminology, "inversion in γ", should now be clear. It is also clear now that if λ is any line which misses γ, then $\lambda^{\text{inv}\,\gamma}$ lies wholly interior to the disk bounded by γ. Hence $\lambda^{\text{inv}\,\gamma}$ *cannot* be a line.

In order to provide a geometric interpretation of inversion which makes the inverse of a point easier to visualize than the arithmetic definition, we prove:

4.1.1   PROPOSITION

Let $\gamma = \text{circle}(G, g)$; $H(\neq G)$ and K points collinear with G, where H is interior to the disk bounded by γ and K is exterior to it; and suppose that line segment TH is $\perp GH$ while TK is tangent to γ at T (see Figure 4.2). Then H and K are mutually inverse in γ.

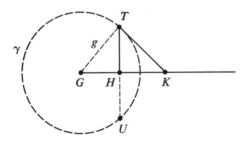

FIGURE 4.2

Proof.   Note that $\triangle GHT \sim \triangle GTK$ (*Important.* This notation means not only that the two triangles mentioned are similar, but also that corresponding vertices are $G \leftrightarrow G$, $H \leftrightarrow T$, $T \leftrightarrow K$.) since they share an angle at G and they have right angles at H and T respectively. ("A line tangent to a circle is perpendicular to the radius drawn to the point of tangency.") Therefore

$$\frac{\text{dist}(G, H)}{\text{dist}(G, T)} = \frac{\text{dist}(G, T)}{\text{dist}(G, K)}.$$

Cross-multiplying gives $\text{dist}(G, H) \cdot \text{dist}(G, K) = g^2$, as desired.   □

4.1.2   COROLLARY

Given $\gamma = \text{circle}(G, g)$ and a point H, you can construct $H^{\text{inv}\,\gamma}$ with ruler and compass.

Proof. When H is interior to the disk bounded by γ (see Figure 4.2 again) there is no difficulty. First draw $HT \perp GH$ and then $TK \perp TG$.

For a point exterior to the disk bounded by γ, K in Figure 4.2, it is merely necessary to draw the two tangents KT and KU to γ and then connect points T and U with a line. One way to find T and U is:

Exercise. Prove: T and U are the points where the circle with GK as diameter meets γ.

Exercise. Divide a radius of $\gamma = \text{circle}(G, 6)$ into six equal parts with points of division H_i as in Figure 4.3. Then find each $H_i' = H_i^{\text{inv}\,\gamma}$ using the definition of inversion. Check some of these points by Proposition 4.1.1.

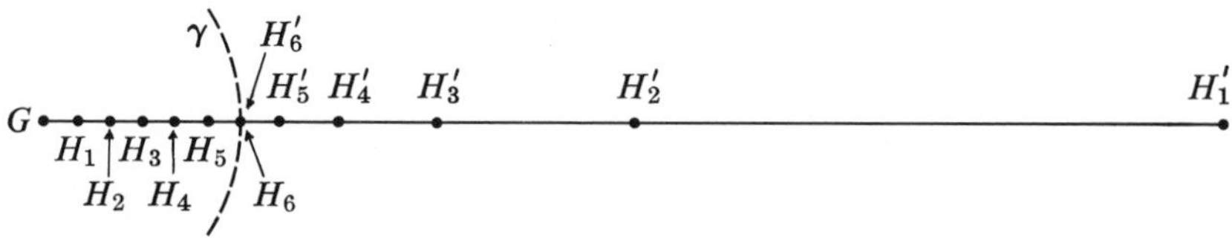

FIGURE 4.3

Note, in Figure 4.3, how inversion "spreads out" points near the center of inversion. A non-mathematical explanation is that since $H_1, H_2, ..., H_6$ are equally spaced between G and γ, then their inverses must be "equally spaced between γ and ∞". A more precise analysis of this spreading out is given in Problems 1, 2, and 3 at the end of this section.

Inversion throws an interesting sidelight on a theorem known to the ancient Greeks:

4.1.3   PROPOSITION   The Circle of Apollonius

Let H and K be distinct points in the plane and let p be a positive real number. Then the set of all points Z such that $\text{dist}(Z, K) = p\,\text{dist}(Z, H)$ is:

(i)   (If $p \neq 1$) a circle γ whose center is on line HK. In this case H and K are mutually inverse points in γ.

(ii) (If $p = 1$) the perpendicular bisector γ of line segment HK. In this case H and K are reflections of each other in γ.

Proof. (ii) is merely a restatement of the familiar theorem that the set of points equally distant from two given points is the perpendicular bisector of the line segment joining those points.

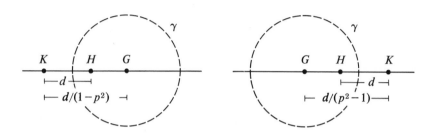

FIGURE 4.4   where $(p < 1)$ **FIGURE 4.5**   where $(p > 1)$

The power of coordinate geometry is illustrated by the fact that it reduces the proof of the first assertion of (i) to a routine exercise (Another proof, using the complex numbers, will be found in Problem 8 of Section 4.2.):

Exercise. Let $d = \text{dist}(H, K)$ and introduce the rectangular coordinate system for which $H = (0, 0)$ and $K = (d, 0)$. Then find γ.

The answer to the above exercise will be $\gamma = \text{circle}(G, g)$, where $G = (d/(1 - p^2), 0)$ and $g = |dp/(1 - p^2)|$. This is illustrated in Figures 4.4 and 4.5, the distances shown being undirected distances (In particular, $\text{dist}(G, H) =$ the *absolute value* of the x-coordinate of G.). It is now easy to compute:

(in Figure 4.4) $\text{dist}(G, K) = d/(1 - p^2) - d = dp^2/(1 - p^2)$
(in Figure 4.5) $\text{dist}(G, K) = d/(p^2 - 1) + d = dp^2/(p^2 - 1)$

so that, in either case, $\text{dist}(G, H) \cdot \text{dist}(G, K) = d^2p^2/(1 - p^2)^2 = g^2$, showing that H and K are mutually inverse in γ. □

In the following problems $\gamma = \text{circle}(G, g)$ is a given circle.

Problem 1. Let HK be a line segment of fixed length d which is allowed to slide along a ray beginning at G (H being between G and K) and let $x = \text{dist}(G, H)$. Show that $y = \text{dist}(H^{\text{inv}\,\gamma}, K^{\text{inv}\,\gamma})$ always increases when x decreases (Figure 4.6).

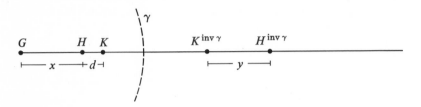

FIGURE 4.6

Problem 2. Let H and K be points collinear with G, H being between G and K, and let $\text{dist}(G, K) \leq g$ (Figure 4.6 again). Show that $\text{dist}(H, K) < \text{dist}(H^{\text{inv}\,\gamma}, K^{\text{inv}\,\gamma})$. Conclude that every point H interior to the disk bounded by γ is closer to γ than is $H^{\text{inv}\,\gamma}$.

Problem 3*. In Figure 4.7, $\text{dist}(H, L) = \text{dist}(H, K)$, and $HL \perp HK$, all three points H, K, L being interior to the disk bounded by γ. Show that $\text{dist}(H', L') > \text{dist}(H', K')$, primes denoting "inv γ". (*Hint.* Use similar triangles to express $\text{dist}(H', L')$ in terms of G, H, L, L', and g.)

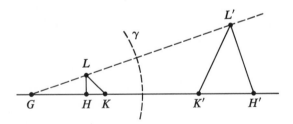

FIGURE 4.7

Problem 4. Let H and K be distinct, mutually inverse points in γ. Show that γ is the set of all points Z such that

$$\frac{\text{dist}(Z, K)}{\text{dist}(Z, H)} = \frac{\text{dist}(G, K)}{g}.$$

(This gives a geometric interpretation of the number p which appears in the Circle of Apollonius.) (*Hint.* Draw radius GZ and look for similar triangles.)

Problem 5. Show that, for any mutually inverse points H and K in γ, and any similarity f of the plane,

$$(H^f)^{\text{inv}\,\gamma^f} = K^f.$$

Conclude that any symmetry f of a curve δ which is also a symmetry of γ is a symmetry of $\delta^{\text{inv}\,\gamma}$, too.

Problem 6*. Let δ be any circle which contains two distinct points H and K which are mutually inverse in γ, and let P be one of the points where δ meets γ. Show that the line tangent to γ at P passes through the center of δ.

4.2   INVERSES OF CIRCLES, LINES, AND ANGLES

Our first task in this section will be to find the inverses of circles and lines. We will prove the main results analytically, by means of the complex numbers. They can also be proved purely geometrically, mainly by properties of similar triangles. The analytic proofs have the advantage that they avoid endless consideration of special cases (resulting, for example, from the fact that each of some pair of points can be inside, on, or outside of some circle). Another advantage is that they "find the answer" while the geometric ones often have the flavor that they are merely proving a known answer to be correct. Nevertheless, the purely geometric proofs have a beauty and simplicity which makes them impossible to ignore; consequently they will be given as second proofs in the form of exercises with hints.

The first step is to interpret inversion in terms of the arithmetic of the complex numbers.

4.2.1   LEMMA

Let $\gamma = \text{circle }(0, g)$ where 0 is the origin. Then $Z^{\text{inv}\,\gamma} = g^2/\bar{Z}$ for every complex number $Z \neq 0$.

Proof. The complex number $Z^{\text{inv}\,\gamma}$ that we want is the one whose absolute value (= distance from 0) is

$$g^2/\text{dist}(0, Z) = g^2/|Z|$$

and whose polar angle is the same as the polar angle θ of Z.

The first condition is met by g^2/Z (see Chapter 2, the exercise after Corollary 2.2.5); however the polar angle of g^2/Z is $0 - \theta = -\theta$. This angle can be corrected by reflecting g^2/Z is the real axis, that is, by taking its complex conjugate (see Remarks 3.2.8)). ▯

The next step is to describe circles and lines by equations.

4.2.2   PROPOSITION

Let A, B, C, and D be complex numbers with $AD - BC \neq 0$. Then the set γ of all complex numbers Z such that

(1) $$|AZ + B| = |CZ + D|$$

is either

(i) (If $|A| \neq |C|$) a circle, or

(ii) (If $|A| = |C|$) a line (namely, the perpendicular bisector of the line segment joining $- B/A$ to $- D/C$).

Every circle and every line has an equation of the above form.

Proof. Since $AD - BC \neq 0$, at least one of A and C must be nonzero.

Case 1. $A \neq 0$ and $C = 0$. (Similar reasoning will apply to the case $A = 0$, $C \neq 0$.) Then (1) takes the form, after division by $|A|$ and use of the formula $|U/V| = |U|/|V|$,

(2) $$|Z + B/A| = |D|/|A|$$

which can be rewritten, more geometrically, in the form

(3) $$\text{dist}(Z, - B/A) = |D/A|.$$

In other words,

(4) $$\gamma = \text{circle}(- B/A, |D/A|).$$

Case 2. $A \neq 0 \neq C$. Here we divide both sides of (1) by $|A|$ and write the result in the form

(5) $$|Z + (B/A)| = \frac{|C|}{|A|}|Z + (D/C)|.$$

This can be rewritten

(6)
$$\text{dist}(Z, -B/A) = \frac{|C|}{|A|} \text{dist}(Z, -D/C)$$

which we recognize as either a Circle of Apollonius (if $|C|/|A| \neq 1$) or the line mentioned in (ii) (if $|C|/|A| = 1$). (See Proposition 4.1.3.) Note that in the latter case the perpendicular bisector doesn't exist when $B/A = D/C$. However this possibility cannot occur because $AD - BC \neq 0$.

Finally, we note that every circle and every line actually has at least one description in the form (1). For circle (G, g) we have the equation $|Z - G| = g(= |0Z + g|)$. If γ is a given line, let $-B$ and $-D$ be points which are reflections of each other in γ. Then equation (1) with $A = C = 1$ describes γ. ⬜

4.2.3   THEOREM

Let $\gamma = $ circle (G, g) and let δ be a circle or a line (possibly punctured at G). Then $\delta^{\text{inv}\,\gamma}$ is a circle or a line (possibly punctured at G).

Caution.   It is important to interpret the "possibly punctured" items correctly. Since $G^{\text{inv}\,\gamma}$ has not been defined, any curve δ containing G must be punctured at G before the symbol $\delta^{\text{inv}\,\gamma}$ is meaningful. Similarly, a line or circle containing G can be the inverse of some curve *only after* G itself has been removed.

Proof.   Introduce a coordinate system with the origin at G. By 4.2.2 there exist complex numbers A, B, C, D with $AD - BC \neq 0$ such that δ is the set of all points Z for which

(1)
$$|AZ + B| = |CZ + D|.$$

We will do the necessary "puncturing" by making the restriction $Z \neq 0$, which will be in force for the remainder of this proof.

Now take any point Z of $\delta^{\text{inv}\,\gamma}$. This is the same as saying that $Z^{\text{inv}\,\gamma}$ is an arbitrary point of δ. Hence we can find the equation of $\delta^{\text{inv}\,\gamma}$ by substituting $Z^{\text{inv}\,\gamma} = g^2/\bar{Z}$ for Z in (1).

$$|(Ag^2/\bar{Z}) + B| = |(Cg^2/\bar{Z}) + D|.$$

Multiply both sides by $|\bar{Z}|$, using the formula $|U| \cdot |V| = |UV|$.

$$|Ag^2 + B\bar{Z}| = |Cg^2 + D\bar{Z}|.$$

Finally, use the formula $|U| = |\bar{U}|$ to get

(2) $$|\bar{B}Z + \bar{A}g^2| = |\bar{D}Z + \bar{C}g^2|$$

which is the equation of a circle or a line (by 4.2.2), as desired. $\square$

4.2.4   REMARKS

We now outline a "four question inversion procedure" for finding the inverse of a given circle or line δ in $\gamma = \text{circle}(G, g)$. This will be followed by a series of examples of the inverses of specific circles δ.

First. "Is $\delta^{\text{inv}\,\gamma}$ a circle or a line?" Since a curve known to be a circle or a line is a line $\Leftrightarrow$ it goes "off to ∞" we see that $\delta^{\text{inv}\,\gamma}$ is a line $\Leftrightarrow$ unpunctured δ contains G. This gives "Question 1" below.

Second. If points H and K are reflections of each other in some line through the center of γ, then $H^{\text{inv}\,\gamma}$ and $K^{\text{inv}\,\gamma}$ will also be reflections of each other in that line (Figure 4.8). This gives "Question 2" (a special case of Problem 5, Section 1).

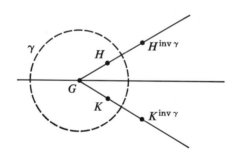

FIGURE 4.8

Question 1. Does unpunctured δ contain G? If "yes", $\delta^{\text{inv}\,\gamma}$ is a line; if "no" a circle.

Question 2. Is δ symmetric with respect to some line through G? If "yes", then $\delta^{\text{inv}\,\gamma}$ is symmetric with respect to that same line.

Question 3. Does δ go "off to ∞"? If "yes", unpunctured $\delta^{\text{inv}\,\gamma}$ contains G.

Question 4. What are the inverses of some specific, strategically selected points of δ?

4.2.5   EXAMPLE

Find $\delta^{\mathrm{inv}\,\gamma}$ where δ is a circle through G (and punctured at G).

Here $\delta^{\mathrm{inv}\,\gamma}$ is a line ("Question 1"). This line must be symmetric with respect to the line of centers GD, since δ is symmetric with respect to this line ("Question 2"); in simpler language: $\delta^{\mathrm{inv}\,\gamma} \perp$ line GD. Thus, in order to draw $\delta^{\mathrm{inv}\,\gamma}$ we only need one point on it ("Question 4"). $Q^{\mathrm{inv}\,\gamma}$ always will do (Figures 4.9 and 4.10) and it can easily be found by Proposition 4.1.1. However, in Figure 4.10 it will be easier to draw line AB.

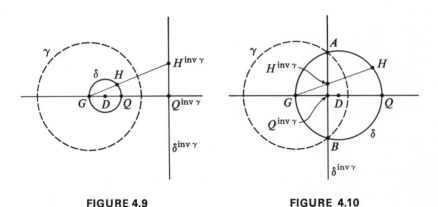

FIGURE 4.9   **FIGURE 4.10**

Problem 1. Give a purely geometric proof (that is, do not use 4.2.3 or the complex numbers) that when $\delta = \mathrm{circle}(D, d)$ passes through G, then $\delta^{\mathrm{inv}\,\gamma}$ is a line $\perp$ line GD. (*Hint.* Show $\triangle GHQ \sim \triangle GQ^{\mathrm{inv}\,\gamma} H^{\mathrm{inv}\,\gamma}$ and hence line $H^{\mathrm{inv}\,\gamma} Q^{\mathrm{inv}\,\gamma} \perp$ line GD.)

4.2.6   EXAMPLE

Let δ be a line *not* passing through the center G of γ. Then $\delta^{\mathrm{inv}\,\gamma}$ *is a circle through G and punctured at G. The center of $\delta^{\mathrm{inv}\,\gamma}$ lies on the perpendicular from G to δ.*

Exercise. Give a proof of 4.2.6 analogous to that of 4.2.5 and draw a diagram.

4.2.7   EXAMPLE

Let $\delta = \text{circle}(D, d)$ *not* pass through the center G of γ. Find $\delta^{\text{inv}\,\gamma}$.

Here (see Figures 4.11 and 4.12) Questions 1 and 3 show that $\delta^{\text{inv}\,\gamma}$ *is a circle not passing through* G. Also, δ is its own reflection in line GD. Hence ("Question 2") so is $\delta^{\text{inv}\,\gamma}$. In other words, *the center of* $\delta^{\text{inv}\,\gamma}$ *lies on the line of centers of* γ *and* δ. Inversion of the points Q and R will now suffice to find $\delta^{\text{inv}\,\gamma}$.

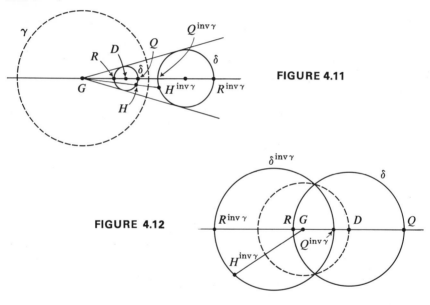

FIGURE 4.11

FIGURE 4.12

Exercise. Show that, in 4.2.7, $D^{\text{inv}\,\gamma}$ is never the center of $\delta^{\text{inv}\,\gamma}$. (*Hint.* Apply Problem 1, Section 4.1 to line segment DQ.)

Problem 2*. Give a purely geometric proof of 4.2.7. (*Hint.* Let $b = [\text{dist}(G, Q) \cdot \text{dist}(G, R)]^{1/2}$ and $\beta = \text{circle}(G, b)$. Show that (a) $\delta^{\text{inv}\,\beta} = \delta$, that (b) $\text{inv}\,\gamma = (\text{inv}\,\beta) \circ G(g^2/b^2)$, and finally (c) use the fact that similarities are circle-preserving (Section 3.3).

Problem 3. (a) Given circles γ and δ as in Figure 4.11 construct $\delta^{\text{inv}\,\gamma}$

with ruler and compass. (Note the relative positions of $D^{\text{inv}\,\gamma}$ and center $\delta^{\text{inv}\,\gamma}$.)

(b) Do the same construction for the situation shown in Figure 4.12.

4.2.8   EXAMPLE

One case remains: δ is a line through G and punctured at G. Here it is obvious that $\delta^{\text{inv}\,\gamma} = \delta$.

So much for inverses of circles and lines!

Our next task will be to analyze what happens to the angle between two curves when the curves are inverted.

DEFINITIONS AND NOTATION

Let two rays $\overrightarrow{HK}$ and $\overrightarrow{HL}$ be given (Figure 4.13). The symbol $\measuredangle\, KHL$ will represent the *number of degrees in the directed angle from ray $\overrightarrow{HK}$ to $\overrightarrow{HL}$,* where the direction of the arrowhead is a reminder that a positive number of degrees indicates a counterclockwise rotation. In Figure 4.13 we make the convention that the solid arc and the dotted arc represent the *same directed angle*. This will be expressed numerically, for the angle actually shown in Figure 4.13, by $\measuredangle\, KHL = 310° = -50°$.

Next, let δ be a curve *leading out* of a point H (Figure 4.14), by which we will mean that δ "reaches" H but does not cross it. A ray $\overrightarrow{HL}$ will be called

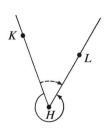

FIGURE 4.13

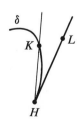

FIGURE 4.14

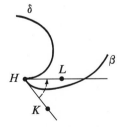

FIGURE 4.15

the ray tangent to δ at H if it is the limiting position of ray $\overrightarrow{HK}$ as K approaches H along $δ$; that is, if ∡ *KHL* approaches 0° as K approaches L along $δ$ (Figure 4.14).

Finally, if we are given two curves $β$ and $δ$ leading out of H and both of which have tangent rays at H, rays $\overrightarrow{HK}$ and $\overrightarrow{HL}$ respectively in Figure 4.15, we define the number of degrees in the *directed angle from β to δ at H* to be ∡ *KHL*.

We will avoid the subtle and difficult question of when tangent rays exist (which would detour us too far from the study of inversion) by restricting our attention to those curves and points where they do exist.

Note that the tangent ray to a line segment HK at H is ray $\overrightarrow{HK}$. Also if $δ$ in Figure 4.14 is an arc of a circle $δ'$, then the tangent ray $\overrightarrow{HL}$ to $δ$ at H is part of the unique straight line through H which meets circle $δ'$ exactly once.

4.2.9   LEMMA

Let H, K, L be complex numbers with K and $L \neq H$. Then ∡ *KHL* is the polar angle of the complex number $(L - H)/(K - H)$ (Figure 4.16).

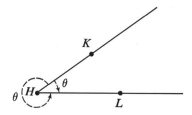

FIGURE 4.16

Exercise. To clarify the meaning of the lemma, compute $(L - H)/(K - H)$ where $H = 1 + i$, $K = 2 + 3i$, and $L = 6 - 9i$. Then compare (on graph paper) the angles which the lemma claims are equal.

Proof.   The idea of the proof is to move the points K, H, and L, without changing $θ = $ ∡*KHL*, to a position where the answer is obvious.

First, note that for any translation t, ∡ *KHL* = ∡*K'H'L'*. Taking

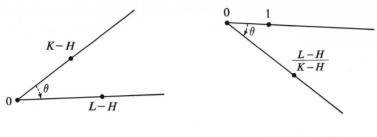

FIGURE 4.17   **FIGURE 4.18**

$t = \mathrm{trans}(\overrightarrow{H0})$ we see that (Figure 4.17) $\theta = \sphericalangle (K - H)\, 0\, (L - H)$. (*To inter-pret this notation properly* remember that the symbol $\sphericalangle$ is followed by three points. Here these points are $K - H$, 0, and $L - H$.) Next, note that if s is any stretch rotation *centered at* 0, then $\theta = \sphericalangle (K - H)^s\, 0\, (L - H)^s$. Taking s to be multiplication by $1/(K - H)$ (Theorem 2.2.4 asserts that this s is a stretch rotation about 0), we see that

$$\theta = \sphericalangle (1)\,(0)\left(\frac{L - H}{K - H}\right)$$

(Figure 4.18). In other words, $\theta = $ polar angle $(L - H)/(K - H)$.   □

4.2.10   LEMMA

Let $\gamma = \mathrm{circle}(G, g)$ and let H, K, L be distinct points $\neq G$. Then

$$\sphericalangle K^{\mathrm{inv}\,\gamma}H^{\mathrm{inv}\,\gamma}L^{\mathrm{inv}\,\gamma} = -\sphericalangle KHL + \sphericalangle KGL.$$

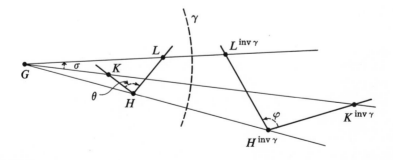

FIGURE 4.19

Before beginning the proof note that, for the particular angles shown in Figure 4.19, the number of degrees θ is negative (alternatively, between 180° and 360°).

Proof. Introduce a coordinate system with the origin at G. By the preceding lemma, the angle φ we want is the polar angle of the complex number

(1) $\dfrac{L^{\text{inv}\gamma} - H^{\text{inv}\gamma}}{K^{\text{inv}\gamma} - H^{\text{inv}\gamma}} = \dfrac{g^2/\bar{L} - g^2/\bar{H}}{g^2/\bar{K} - g^2/\bar{H}}$ (using 4.2.1)

$= \text{(after simplification)} \dfrac{L - \bar{H}}{\bar{K} - \bar{H}} \cdot \dfrac{\bar{K}}{\bar{L}} = \overline{\left(\dfrac{L - H}{K - H}\right)} \cdot \overline{\left(\dfrac{K - 0}{L - 0}\right)}$

(the student is urged to work out all the details). Since $\bar{U}$ is the reflection of U in the real axis, the polar angle of $\bar{U}$ is minus that of U. Hence we recognize (with the help of 4.2.9) the extreme right-hand side of (1) to be the complex number whose polar angle is $-\sphericalangle KHL - \sphericalangle LOK$ as desired. $\square$

Note that this means that, in Figure 4.19, $\varphi = -\theta$ *only when K and L are collinear with G.* However, when σ is near 0° then φ nearly equals $-\theta$. This suggest taking a limit and gives our final result, which is quite surprising in view of the way that inversion changes distances:

4.2.11 THEOREM

Let β and δ be curves leading out of a point H and each of which has a tangent ray at H. Then for any $\gamma = \text{circle}(G, g)$ with $G \neq H$, both $\beta^{\text{inv}\gamma}$ and $\delta^{\text{inv}\gamma}$ have tangent rays at $H^{\text{inv}\gamma}$, and the directed angle from $\beta^{\text{inv}\gamma}$ to $\delta^{\text{inv}\gamma}$ at H equals minus the directed angle from β to δ at H (see Figure 4.20).

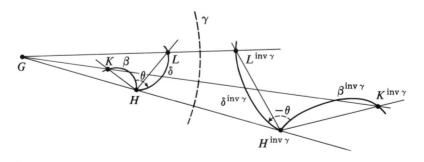

FIGURE 4.20

Proof. Suppose, for the time being, that we know that the inverted curves have tangent rays at $H^{\text{inv}\,\gamma}$. We want to show that the angle from one to the other is $-\theta$. The difficulty in this proof is that we cannot get the tangent rays by merely inverting the tangent rays to β and δ at H. (Straight lines don't usually remain straight under inversion.)

Let K and L be points $\neq H$ or G on β and δ respectively. Then by Lemma 4.2.10,

$$(1) \qquad \sphericalangle\, K^{\text{inv}\,\gamma} H^{\text{inv}\,\gamma} L^{\text{inv}\,\gamma} = -\sphericalangle\, KHL + \sphericalangle\, KGL.$$

Now let K and L approach the limiting position H along β and δ respectively. Then $K^{\text{inv}\,\gamma}$ and $L^{\text{inv}\,\gamma}$ approach $H^{\text{inv}\,\gamma}$ along the inverses of β and δ. Since these inverted curves have tangent rays at $H^{\text{inv}\,\gamma}$, rays $\overrightarrow{H^{\text{inv}\,\gamma} K^{\text{inv}\,\gamma}}$ and $\overrightarrow{H^{\text{inv}\,\gamma} L^{\text{inv}\,\gamma}}$ will approach these tangent rays. Hence the angle we want is the limit of (1) as K and L approach H; and this is $-\sphericalangle\, KHL + 0°$ as desired. ☐

Exercise. Prove that the claimed tangent rays exist. (*Hint.* Just do it for δ. Let M be any point $\neq G$ and $\neq H$ on line segment GH and consider the limit of $\sphericalangle\, M^{\text{inv}\,\gamma} H^{\text{inv}\,\gamma} L^{\text{inv}\,\gamma}$ as L approaches H.)

One consequence of the theorem is the determination of those circles which are their own inverses.

4.2.12   COROLLARY

Let $\gamma = \text{circle}(G, g)$ and let δ be any circle $\neq \gamma$. The following assertions about δ are equivalent.[†]
   (i) $\delta = \delta^{\text{inv}\,\gamma}$.
   (ii) δ contains a pair of distinct points which are mutually inverse in γ.
   (iii) $\delta \perp \gamma$.

Proof.   (i) → (iii). Let the two points be H and K, as in Figure 4.21. Then δ must meet γ at a point T between H and K. Let U be any point of γ which is "near" T.

By the theorem, undirected angle φ equals undirected angle θ. Since $\theta + \varphi = 180°$ we must have $\theta = \varphi = 90°$ as claimed in (iii).

[†] "Equivalent" means that if one of the statements is true, then all are true.

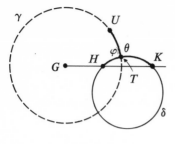

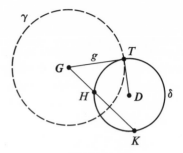

FIGURE 4.21   **FIGURE 4.22**

(iii) → (ii). Let T be one of the points of intersection of γ and δ. Since a tangent line to a circle is perpendicular to the radius drawn to the point of tangency, the hypothesis $\delta \perp \gamma$ shows that the tangent to δ at T passes through the center G of γ. Thus GT is tangent to δ at T (Figure 4.22). Statement (ii) is now an immediate consequence of the theorem of elementary plane geometry which states: *The product of a secant* (GK) *from a point* (G) *to a circle by its external segment* (GH) *equals the square of the tangent* (GT) *drawn from that point to the circle.* Readers unfamiliar with this theorem can readily construct its proof by looking for similar triangles in Figure 4.23.

(ii) → (i). By the theorem in italics above, the product $GH \cdot GK$ in Figure 4.22 has the same value for every choice of distinct points H and K collinear with G, namely, the square of the tangent from G to δ. By (ii) this product equals g^2 for some *particular* choice of H and K, hence for every choice of H and K. Thus (i) holds. ☐

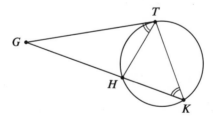

FIGURE 4.23

4.2.13   REMARK

Corollary 4.2.12 provides another way to visualize the inverse $K = H^{\text{inv}\,\gamma}$ of a point H; namely, $H^{\text{inv}\,\gamma}$ is the "second intersection" of any two circles through H which are $\perp \gamma$. (See Figure 4.22. When $H = T$, we define this "second intersection" to be T.) Alternatively, $H^{\text{inv}\,\gamma}$ is the second intersection of line GH with any one of those circles.

Note that if γ is a line instead of a circle, this "second intersection" property defines $H^{\text{refl}\,\gamma}$. Thus inversion provides an extension to circles of the notion of reflection in a line.

Problem 4*. Use 4.2.13 and the theorem to prove Corollary 4.2.14.

4.2.14   COROLLARY

Let H and K be mutually inverse points in $\gamma = \text{circle}(G, g)$ and let $\delta = \text{circle}$ (D, d) and suppose the points H, K, G, and D are distinct. Then

   (i) (If D is not a point of γ) $H^{\text{inv}\,\delta}$ and $K^{\text{inv}\,\delta}$ are mutually inverse points in circle $\gamma^{\text{inv}\,\delta}$.

   (ii) (If D is a point of γ) $H^{\text{inv}\,\delta}$ and $K^{\text{inv}\,\delta}$ are reflections of each other in line $\gamma^{\text{inv}\,\delta}$.

4.2.15   THE INVERSIVE PLANE

In closing this section we introduce some new terminology which makes it easier to remember some of the theorems of this chapter. By the *inversive plane* we will mean the Euclidean plane together with one additional point, called the *point at infinity*. (*Notation.* ∞.) By an *inversive circle* we will mean either an ordinary circle, or a straight line together with ∞. If γ is a given (ordinary) circle centered at G, we define $G^{\text{inv}\,\gamma} = \infty$ and $\infty^{\,\text{inv}\,\gamma} = G$. Finally, if γ is an inversive circle through ∞ (that is, a line together with ∞) we define inv γ to mean refl γ (see 4.2.13) and interpret this to mean that ∞ is its own reflection in every line.

The theorem about inversion of circles and lines (4.2.3) can now be stated more simply: Let γ be an inversive circle. Then for every inversive circle δ, $\delta^{\text{inv}\,\gamma}$ is again an inversive circle. No remarks have to be made about when to puncture δ or $\delta^{\text{inv}\,\gamma}$ or about when it becomes a line (i.e. when it contains ∞).

Once we have this new terminology, the "Circle of Apollonius" Proposition (4.1.3) no longer requires the statement of a special case for

$p = 1$, nor does Corollary 4.2.14 require 2 cases; and the statement, "Each three distinct points lie on exactly one inversive circle," does not have any exceptions (its Euclidean version does). In addition, the fact that inversion reverses angles (4.2.11) becomes an extension of the fact that reflection reverses angles.

We will return to the inversive plane in Sections 4.3 and 4.4.

Problem 5. Let Z be any complex number and let $\gamma = $ circle (gi, g). Find the limit, as g approaches ∞, of $Z^{\text{inv}\,\gamma}$. (*Hint.* Start with the formula $Z^{\text{inv}\,\gamma} = g^2/(\bar{Z} - \bar{G}) + G$ for $\gamma = $ circle (G, g).)

Problem 6. Let $\gamma = $ circle (G, g) and let H and K be distinct points $\neq G$. Derive the formula

$$\text{dist}(H^{\text{inv}\,\gamma}, K^{\text{inv}\,\gamma}) = g^2 \, \frac{\text{dist}(H, K)}{\text{dist}(G, H) \cdot \text{dist}(G, K)}$$

(a) by using the complex numbers (put the origin at G), and (b) by similar triangles. (To avoid too many diagrams for part (b), consider only the case that H and K are interior to the disk bounded by γ and not collinear with G.)

4.2.16 REMARK

In Problem 6, let H be a fixed point, K a variable point. Then we see, from Problem 6, that $\text{dist}(H^{\text{inv}\,\gamma}, K^{\text{inv}\,\gamma})$ depends not only upon the variable $\text{dist}(H, K)$, but also upon how far K is from G. However,

$$\lim_{K \to H} \frac{\text{dist}(H^{\text{inv}\,\gamma}, K^{\text{inv}\,\gamma})}{\text{dist}(H, K)} = \left[\frac{g}{\text{dist}(G, H)} \right]^2$$

regardless of the direction of approach $K \to H$. Hence a very small triangle HKL will be transformed by inv γ to a figure which is *approximately a triangle similar to* $\triangle HKL$. The number $[g/\text{dist}(G, H)]^2$ is sometimes called the "ratio of magnification of inv γ near H". When H is on γ this ratio equals 1, hence γ is sometimes called the *isometric circle* of inv γ.

Problem 7. Let H and K be distinct complex numbers. Show that the points Z on line HK are precisely the points

$$Z = t \cdot H + (1 - t) \cdot K \qquad \text{where } t \text{ ranges through the real numbers.}$$

(*Hint.* By Lemma 3.2.5, the above equation describes a translation or stretch-notation of the real axis.)

Problem 8*. Here is another way of proving the Circle of Apollonius Proposition (4.1.3), and deriving the equations of circles in terms of the complex numbers (4.2.2). It has the advantage of actually finding the centers and radii of the circles involved; and the necessary computations provide some healthy exercise in complex number arithmetic.

(a) Starting with the formula $|U|^2 = U\bar{U}$, derive the following formula for "completing the conjugate square".

$$Z\bar{Z} + \bar{E}Z + E\bar{Z} + E\bar{E} = |Z + E|^2$$

(b) Let A, B, C, D be given complex numbers with $|A| \neq |C|$ and $AD - BC \neq 0$. Show that the set γ of all complex numbers Z such that

$$|AZ + B| = |CZ + D|$$

is a circle, and find its center and radius. *Hints.* Use the formula $|U|^2 = U \cdot \bar{U}$ to remove the absolute value signs. Then rearrange terms so that, after completion of the conjugate square, the equation takes the form $|Z + G'| = g$. The answer will be

$$\text{center } \gamma = -G' = \frac{-\bar{A}B + \bar{C}D}{|A|^2 - |C|^2}$$

$$\text{radius } \gamma = g = \frac{|AD - BC|}{|A|^2 - |C|^2}$$

(c) Prove, by specializing (b), that the set γ of complex numbers Z such that

$$|Z - K| = p|Z - H|$$

(H, K given complex numbers, p a given positive real number $\neq 1$) is a circle; and find its center and radius in terms of H, K, and p. (*Answer.* center $= [1/(1 - p^2)] \cdot (K - p^2 H)$, radius $= (1/|1 - p^2|) \cdot |K - H|$.)

Problem 9*. (a) Let E be a given complex number, p a positive real number. Show that the set λ of all complex numbers Z such that $\bar{E}Z + E\bar{Z} = p$ is a straight line. (*Hint.* First consider the case $E = 1$.) Express the inclination of this line in terms of E. (*Answer.* The angle from the positive real axis to the perpendicular from the origin to the line equals the polar angle of $-E$.)

(b) Use (a) to show that, when $|A| = |C|$ and $AD - BC \neq 0$, the equation $|AZ + B| = |CZ + D|$ describes a line.

Problem 10. What happens to Statement (i) of Corollary 4.2.14 if $H = D$? Does the terminology of the inversive plane make this exceptional case look "less exceptional"?

4.3   APPLICATION TO GEOMETRY OF CIRCLES

Given two curves β and δ which cross at a point A and have tangent lines at A, we define the *undirected angle between β and δ at A* to be that angle θ between their tangent lines which satisfies $0 \leq \theta \leq 90°$ (see Figure 4.24).

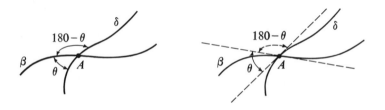

FIGURE 4.24

Note that $\theta = 0°$ means that β and δ are tangent at A. We will write $\beta \perp \delta$ to mean that $\theta = 90°$. The most common terminology for this last situation is: β is *orthogonal to δ at A*, the word "perpendicular" being (somewhat foolishly) reserved for the case that β and δ are lines. Note that when β is a circle and δ is a line, $\beta \perp \delta$ amounts to saying that δ *passes through the center of β*. This is merely a restatement of the familiar theorem: A line tangent to a circle is perpendicular to the radius which is drawn to the point of tangency.

Finally, note that when a circle β meets a line or a circle δ twice, say at H and K, then the undirected angle between β and δ at H equals the angle at K. Hence we can speak unambiguously of *the undirected angle between β and δ* (see Figures 4.25a and 4.25b).

For use in the applications below, we will have to know the number of straight lines which make a pair of specified, undirected angles θ and φ

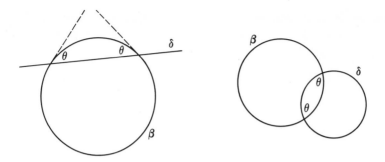

FIGURES 4.25a, b

respectively with two specified non-intersecting circles β and δ, neither lying inside the (disk bounded by the) other (see Figure 4.26).

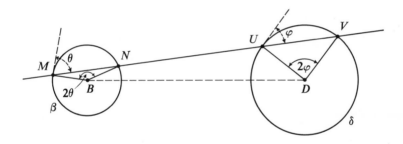

FIGURE 4.26

In order to visualize the angle φ between line UV and circle δ in Figure 4.26, recall that *the number of degrees between a tangent ray and a chord of a circle is half the number of degrees in the arc UV which it intercepts.* Therefore the central angle UDV has 2φ degrees, and we can think of φ as being determined either by this central angle or by the length of chord UV, whichever is more convenient. Therefore the set of all lines which make the given undirected angle of φ degrees with δ are those which can be obtained by rotating line UV about D.

Now consider the other given angle θ and circle β. Begin the above-mentioned rotation with U and V positioned so that line UV is tangent to circle β at (what appears in Figure 4.26 to be) the top of circle β. As line

UV rotates in a counterclockwise direction, θ increases from $0°$ to $90°$ and then decreases again to $0°$, as can be seen most easily from the behavior of central angle MBN. If the rotation is continued, line UV will miss β for a while, and then run through the angles $0°$ to $90°$ to $0°$ once more before completing $360°$ of rotation. Thus:

4.3.1   PROPOSITION

The number of lines which make given undirected angles θ and φ respectively with given non-intersecting circles β and δ, neither lying inside the other, is 4, 2, or 1 according as none, one, or both of θ and φ equal $90°$.

We can supplement the above proposition by noting that *if β and δ are any circles with distinct centers, then there is exactly one line $\perp$ both β and δ,* namely, their line of centers. We will also need:

4.3.2   PROPOSITION

The lines in Proposition 4.3.1 can be constructed with ruler and compass from the following given data: the center and radius of β and of γ and the angles θ and φ.

Proof. (Note that "ruler and compass' really means "unmarked straight edge and compass".) Figure 4.27 shows the given angles, from which we wish to construct line $MNUV$ of Figure 4.26. (The other "solution lines" can be constructed by slight alterations in the procedure given below.)

Since points B and D (and hence line segment BD) are known, we only have to find angle MBD: Then we can find point M, then point N (central angle $MBN = 2\theta$) and hence line MN. The method of finding angle MBD will be to work backwards, drawing a horizontal copy of line MN and then finding the resulting position of D.

First construct isosceles triangle $B_1 M_1 N_1$ with vertex angle 2θ and equal legs of length $b =$ radius β, as in Figure 4.27. (We put off, to the second exercise below, what modifications must be made when θ or $\varphi = 0°$ or $90°$.) Similarly construct isosceles triangle $D_0 U_0 V_0$ with $d =$ radius δ (Figure 4.27 again). Then, on line $M_1 N_1$ as base (see Figure 4.28) construct two copies, $D_2 U_2 V_2$ and $D_3 U_3 V_3$, of triangle $D_0 U_0 V_0$. The distance from dotted line $D_2 D_3$ to line $M_1 N_1$ is the same as the distance from point D to the desired line MN of Figure 4.26. Hence if we let D_1 be the point on this dotted line

FIGURE 4.27

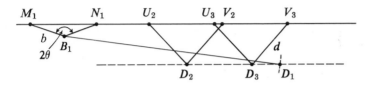

FIGURE 4.28

such that $\text{dist}(B_1, D_1) = \text{dist}(B, D)$ [found by drawing a circle centered at B_1 and of radius $\text{dist}(B, D)$], the desired angle will be $M_1 B_1 D_1$. ☐

Exercise. Carry out the above construction with $\theta = 30°$, $\varphi = 45°$ and any β and δ.

Exercise. Describe how the above construction must be modified when θ or $\varphi = 0°$, when θ but not $\varphi = 90°$, and when $\theta = \varphi = 90°$.

Now, for the first application of inversion, we start with the same two given angles θ and φ and circles β and δ, but we allow ourselves an extra degree of freedom by allowing β and δ to be cut by a circle or a line ε. When this is done, what happens to the numbers 4, 2, 1? Do we gain enough freedom to satisfy an additional condition such as making ε pass through a given point?

Let β and δ be non-intersecting circles. We will say that a point G is *between* β and δ if it is on neither of them, and if there is a circular arc or line segment from G to each of β and δ which does not cross the other (Figures 4.29 and 4.30). We will say that G is *separated* by β from δ if G is a point of neither β nor δ and if every circular arc or line segment which connects G to δ must intersect β (Figures 4.32, 4.33, and 4.34).

Exercise. Find a circle ε which inverts Figure 4.29 into a pair of circles, one inside the other (as in Figure 4.30) and G to a point outside δ but inside β. (*Hint.* There will be infinitely many such circles.)

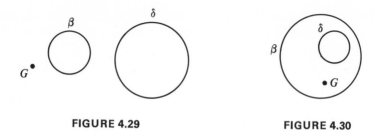

FIGURE 4.29   **FIGURE 4.30**

4.3.3   THEOREM

The number of circles and lines ε which make given undirected angles θ and φ respectively with distinct given non-intersecting circles β and δ and pass through a given point G between these circles is 4, 2, or 1 according as none, one, or both of θ and φ equal 90°. These circles and lines can be constructed with ruler and compass.

Proof. Invert Figures 4.29 and 4.30 in any circle centered at G. Then $\beta^{\mathrm{inv}\,\gamma}$ and $\delta^{\mathrm{inv}\,\gamma}$ are again non-intersecting circles (by 4.2.7). Furthermore, neither is interior to the disk bounded by the other: Since G is between β and δ, $\infty = G^{\mathrm{inv}\,\gamma}$ must be between $\beta^{\mathrm{inv}\,\gamma}$ and $\delta^{\mathrm{inv}\,\gamma}$. (Readers who do not yet trust the inversive plane may prefer to reword this reasoning as follows: There is a circular arc or a line segment α through G which intersects β but not δ. Then $\alpha^{\mathrm{inv}\,\gamma}$ is a ray (by 4.2.5) which intersects $\beta^{\mathrm{inv}\,\gamma}$ but not $\delta^{\mathrm{inv}\,\gamma}$. Similarly there is a ray which intersects $\delta^{\mathrm{inv}\,\gamma}$ but not $\beta^{\mathrm{inv}\,\gamma}$, and this shows that neither inverted circle can be interior to the disk bounded by the other.)

Now let ε be any circle or line through G which makes the required angles with β and δ. Then $\varepsilon^{\mathrm{inv}\,\gamma}$ is a *line* which makes these same (undirected) angles with $\beta^{\mathrm{inv}\,\gamma}$ and $\delta^{\mathrm{inv}\,\gamma}$ (by 4.2.11) (see Figure 4.31). Conversely, given

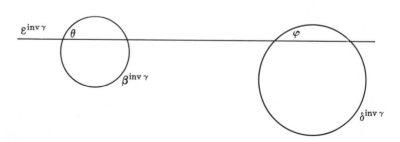

FIGURE 4.31

any line $\varepsilon^{\text{inv}\,\gamma}$ (in Figure 4.31) which cuts $\beta^{\text{inv}\,\gamma}$ and $\delta^{\text{inv}\,\gamma}$ at the required angles, we get, by inversion in γ, a line or circle ε through G which makes the required angles with β and γ.

Since the number of such lines $\varepsilon^{\text{inv}\,\gamma}$ must be 4, 2, or 1 (Proposition 4.3.1) the number of possibilities for ε is the same. Moreover, since the lines $\varepsilon^{\text{inv}\,\gamma}$ can be constructed with ruler and compass, and points can be inverted with ruler and compass, the desired circles ε can be constructed with ruler and compass. [To construct the inverse of a circle it is enough to construct the inverses of three points. Sometimes even less work is required.]   □

Exercise. Choose a particular G, β, and δ; and a circle γ centered at G and not intersecting either β or δ. Then (a) construct the inverses of β and δ in γ. (b) Using *only a ruler* draw a line (approximately) tangent to $\beta^{\text{inv}\,\gamma}$ and $\delta^{\text{inv}\,\gamma}$. Finally, (c) Verify the theorem by inverting this line; it should be tangent to both β and δ.

The proof of the above theorem is an example of the way in which inversion can demolish a problem whose answer is not at all obvious. We now use inversion to study the role played by the "betweenness" hypothesis of the theorem. Recall that point G is *separated by β from δ* (β and δ non-intersecting circles) if G is a point of neither β nor δ and if every circular arc or line segment connecting G to δ must cross β. (Figures 4.32, 4.33, and 4.34.)

Problem 1. Let β and δ be non-intersecting circles and G a point separated by β from δ. Show that there are angles $\theta > 0°$ such that *no* circle through G which makes an angle of θ with β is tangent to δ. (*Hint.* Invert in a circle centered at G.)

The above problem shows that if the "betweenness" hypothesis is dropped from Theorem 4.3.3, then the list of numbers 4, 2, 1 must be increased to include 0. The next theorem shows that ∞ must also be added to this list.

4.3.4   THEOREM

For any two non-intersecting, non-concentric circles β and δ there are two points G (separated by β from δ) and K (separated by δ from β) such that

the collection
$$\left\{\begin{matrix}\text{all circles} \perp \text{both } \beta \text{ and } \delta \\ \text{and the line } \perp \text{both } \beta \text{ and } \delta\end{matrix}\right\} = \left\{\begin{matrix}\text{all circles containing both } G \text{ and } K \\ \text{and the line containing } G \text{ and } K\end{matrix}\right\}$$

(The points G and K are called the *limiting points* of β and δ).

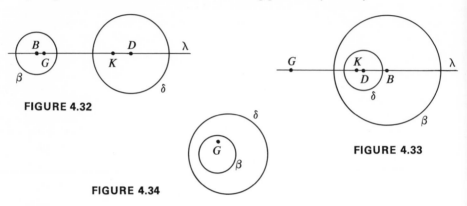

FIGURE 4.32

FIGURE 4.33

FIGURE 4.34

Proof. (See Figures 4.32 and 4.33.) The line $\lambda \perp$ both β and δ is their line of centers. (Note that this last statement tacitly uses the "non-concentric" hypothesis.) The proof of this theorem will be split into two parts. First we choose a single circle ε, $\perp$ both β and δ, and show that it intersects the line of centers λ twice as described in the theorem. Then, calling these points G and K we show that they have the desired properties.

So let ε be any circle $\perp$ both β and δ (such an ε exists by 4.3.3), and consider first the case that neither β nor δ is inside the other (Figure 4.32). Since $\varepsilon \perp \beta$, ε intersects β at 2 points W and X which, we wish to prove, are on opposite sides of λ (and hence ε meets λ inside β as desired).

Therefore consider the consequences of the assumption that W and X are *not* on opposite sides of λ, say they are both below λ (possibly on λ) as in Figure 4.35.

Where is the center E of ε? Since $\varepsilon \perp \beta$ we can find E as the intersection of the lines $\perp$ radii BW and BX at W and X respectively. Hence E is below λ and

(1) E is to the left of (or possibly on) the line μ tangent to β at U
(hence $\perp \lambda$ at U).

Since a circle lies entirely on one side of any line tangent to it, ε lies entirely below both lines BW and BX, hence below λ. It follows that both of the points where ε meets δ must be below λ and hence, by the reasoning used to obtain (1), E must lie to the right of the line v in Figure 4.35. Thus we have arrived at the absurdity that E *is to the left of μ and also to the right of v.*

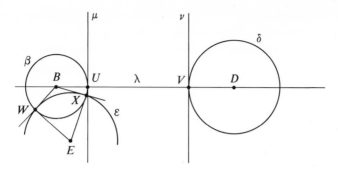

FIGURE 4.35   The impossible case

Hence the assumption that W and X are not on opposite sides of λ was wrong. In simpler language, W and X *are* on opposite sides of λ, and hence ε meets λ at a point G inside β. By similar reasoning we conclude that ε also meets λ at a point K inside (the disk bounded by) δ.

Exercise. Obtain the existence of G and K for the case pictured in Figure 4.32 (δ inside β) by inverting Figure 4.32 in a circle whose center is on λ and between β and δ (This will change Figure 4.33 to Figure 4.32.)

For the second part of the proof, invert either Figure 4.32 or Figure 4.33 in a circle γ centered at G, and let ε be the circle used above to obtain G and K. Then ε' and $\lambda'(=\lambda)$ (primes denoting inv γ) are perpendicular lines. Also, β' and δ' are circles, each $\perp$ both lines ε' and λ'; hence each of these lines passes through the center of *both circles β' and δ'*. The fact that $\varepsilon' \neq \lambda'$ (since $\varepsilon \neq \lambda$) now forces β' and δ' to be concentric, as in Figure 4.36. The

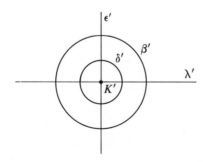

FIGURE 4.36

common center of β' and δ' is found by inverting (in γ) the point of intersection $\neq G$ of ε and λ. Hence it is K' as shown.

It is now clear that the collection of all circles and lines $\perp$ both β' and δ' equals the collection of all lines through K'. Inverting these two descriptions of collections of lines, we get the assertion of the theorem. $\square$

In the course of the above proof we have also established the following fact, which we will need again shortly.

4.3.5   COROLLARY

Let γ be a circle centered at one of the limiting points G of two non-intersecting, non-concentric circles β and δ. Then $\beta^{\mathrm{inv}\,\gamma}$ and $\delta^{\mathrm{inv}\,\gamma}$ are concentric circles.

Exercise. (Same notation as in the theorem) Show that $G^{\mathrm{inv}\,\beta} = K$ and $G^{\mathrm{inv}\,\delta} = K$. (*Answer.* See Remark 4.2.13.)

4.3.6   PROPOSITION

Let G and K be the limiting points of a pair of non-intersecting, non-concentric circles β and δ; and let ε be any circle through G which intersects β and δ. Then there is a circle τ such that

$$\left\{\begin{array}{l}\text{the collection}\\ \text{all circles through } G \text{ which}\\ \text{make the same angles with}\\ \beta \text{ and } \delta \text{ as does } \varepsilon\end{array}\right\} = \left\{\begin{array}{l}\text{the collection}\\ \text{all circles through } G\\ \text{and tangent to } \tau\end{array}\right\}$$

Problem 2. Prove 4.3.6. (*Hint.* Invert in a circle centered at G.) An interesting by-product of the solution will be that, as θ and φ approach $90°$, the circle τ gets "squeezed down" to the limiting point K.

To see the role played by the "non-intersecting" and "non-concentric" hypotheses in the above theorems, the reader is referred to Problems 10 and 11.

For a dramatic, but simple application of inversion we will need the following definitions. Given a point G, a *G-arc* is an arc, not containing G, of a circle passing through G. A *G-triangle* is a geometric figure bounded by three *G*-arcs as in Figure 4.37.

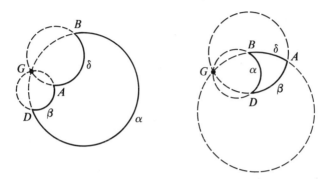

FIGURE 4.37 *G*-triangles *ABD*

4.3.7   THEOREM

The sum of the angles of a *G*-triangle is 180°.

Problem 3. Give a proof. (*Hint.* Invert.)

We now give two theorems about rings of circles. Let β and δ be non-intersecting circles with δ inside β; and let ε_1 be any circle tangent to β and δ as shown in Figure 4.38 (to β internally, to δ externally), ε_2 tangent to ε_1, β, and δ as shown, ε_3 tangent to ε_2, β, and δ but $\varepsilon_3 \neq \varepsilon_1$, and so on. We will call such a sequence of circles $\varepsilon_1, \varepsilon_2, \varepsilon_3, \ldots$, a *Steiner ring of circles between β and δ.* If, by going around δ n times, a Steiner ring returns to ε_1 (that is, some $\varepsilon_t = \varepsilon_1$) we will say that the ring *closes after n revolutions.* It is not difficult to construct Steiner rings which never close. However, the following amusing property holds:

4.3.8   THEOREM   Steiner's Porism

If some Steiner ring of circles between β and δ closes after n revolutions, then so does every Steiner ring between β and δ.

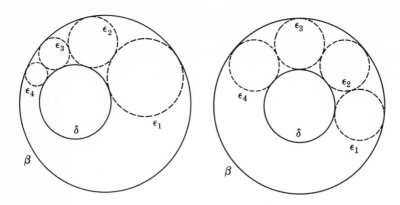

FIGURE 4.38

Proof.   The theorem is obviously true if β and δ are concentric. So suppose they are not. Then they have a pair of limiting points G and K (4.3.4) and when inverted in a circle centered at either of these points they become concentric (4.3.5). Since inversion preserves tangency of circles the theorem is now reduced to the concentric case, where it is obvious.   ☐

Exercise. Show that the points of contact of successive circles in any Steiner ring all lie on a circle. (*Caution.* The centers almost *never* lie on a circle. See Problem 7.)

Exercise. The proof of Steiner's Porism didn't use the hypothesis that δ is inside β. Draw a diagram to illustrate the definition of a "Steiner ring" when neither β nor δ is inside the other. (*Caution.* In this case it may be necessary to allow one or two of the "circles" ε in the ring to be a straight line.)

4.3.9   PROPOSITION   Pappus's Theorem

Let $\beta = \text{circle}(B, b)$ and $\delta = \text{circle}(D, d)$ be internally tangent at T and E_0 the point on line BD midway between the two circles. Then let $\varepsilon_0 = \text{circle}(E_0, e_0)$, $\varepsilon_1 = \text{circle}(E_1, e_1), \ldots$, be a sequence of circles, each tangent to the next and to β and δ as in Figure 4.39. Then the distance d_n from each E_n to the line of centers BD equals $2ne_n$.

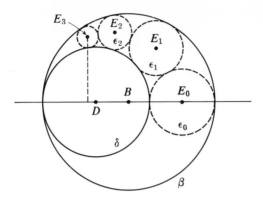

FIGURE 4.39

Problem 4. Give a proof of 4.3.9. (*Hint.* To get $d_3 = 6e_3$, invert in $\tau = $ $= \text{circle}(T, t_3)$ where t_3 is the length of the tangent from T to ε_3, noting that $\varepsilon_3^{\text{inv}\,\tau} = \varepsilon_3$.)

In the constructions of classical Euclidean geometry the useable tools are restricted to an unmarked straight-edge and compass. However, the use of the straight-edge can be regarded as a weakness. For, while the compass actually *draws* a circle, the straight-edge merely *copies* a line segment. We describe, below, a mechanical device which draws a line segment. The idea is to construct a device (called *Peaucellier's cell*) which draws the inverse of any curve it traces, and then to make it trace an arc of a circle whose inverse is known to be a line.

Peaucellier's cell consists of four rods of equal length b, hinged together at P, Y, Q, X as in Figure 4.40 to form a rhombus; and two additional rods of equal length $d > b$, hinged at G, P, and Q. The hinges are perpendicular to the page, so that as the cell "flexes" it remains in the plane.

We will show below that $Y = X^{\text{inv}\,\gamma}$ where $\gamma = \text{circle}(G, \sqrt{d^2 - b^2})$. Hence, if G is held fixed and X traces a curve δ, then Y traces $\delta^{\text{inv}\,\gamma}$. If we now choose an arbitrary point $H \neq G$ in the *plane* and attach it to point X in the *cell* by a rod of length $h = \text{dist}(H, G)$, with a hinge at X, then the motion of X will be restricted to part of $\delta = \text{circle}(H, h)$, as in Figure 4.41, and consequently (since δ contains G) Y will trace part of line $\delta^{\text{inv}\,\gamma}$ (by Example 4.2.5).

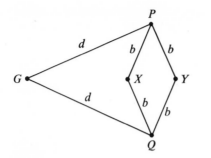

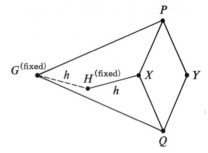

FIGURE 4.40   Peaucellier's cell.   **FIGURE 4.41   Y draws a line segment.**

4.3.10   PROPOSITION

In Peaucellier's cell (Figure 4.40), $X^{\text{inv}\,\gamma} = Y$ where $\gamma = \text{circle}(G, \sqrt{d^2 - b^2})$.

Proof.   Figure 4.42 shows the top half of Peaucellier's cell, and the dotted line is perpendicular to line GXY. By the Pythagorean theorem,

(1) $\qquad\qquad (x + u)^2 + v^2 = d^2 \quad \text{and} \quad (y - u)^2 + v^2 = d^2$

(2) $\qquad\qquad\qquad\qquad u^2 + v^2 = b^2.$

$\qquad$ Subtracting (2) from (1) gives

(3) $\qquad\qquad x^2 + 2ux = d^2 - b^2 \quad \text{and} \quad y^2 - 2uy = d^2 - b^2.$

Thus the roots of the quadratic equation $t^2 + 2ut - (d^2 - b^2) = 0$ are x and $-y$. Since the coefficient of t^2 is 1, the product of the roots of this equation is its constant term: $-xy = -(d^2 - b^2)$ as desired.   □

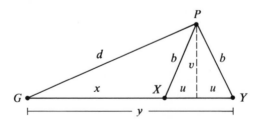

FIGURE 4.42

Exercise. Make a Peaucellier's cell with the extra bar which forces it to draw a line segment.

Our final application answers a question that occurs to many students during their first course in plane geometry:

4.3.11   THE PROBLEM OF APOLLONIUS

Construct (with ruler and compass) *a circle ε tangent to three given non-intersecting circles α, β, and δ, none of which separates the other two* (as in Figures 4.43 and 4.44, but *not* as in Figure 4.45). A little thought will show that there are usually eight such circles ε. In fact, there will always be exactly eight solutions if we allow some of the "circles" ε to be lines. In what follows,

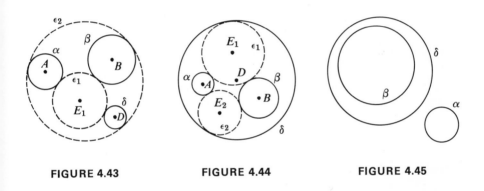

FIGURE 4.43   FIGURE 4.44   FIGURE 4.45

we will consider only those circles ε which *do not separate* the given circles α, β, and δ from each other. However, a slight modification of our procedure will cover the remaining cases.

Solution.   If we can find the centers E_1 and E_2 of ε_1 and ε_2 the rest of the problem becomes a triviality. Note that, in Figure 4.43, if we hold points A, B, D, and E_1 fixed, increase the radii a, b, and d of α, β, and δ respectively by some common amount r, and then *decrease* the radius e_1 of ε_1 by r, the new circle ε_1 will still be tangent to the new α, β, and δ. This is due to the fact that the point of contact of two mutually tangent circles is on their line of centers. The radius of the new e_2 will be old e_2 plus r, as can readily be seen by drawing the diagram containing point E_2. The analogously altered radii for Figure 4.43 are $a + r$, $b + r$, $d - r$, $e_1 - r$, and $e_2 - r$.

We now want to choose r just large enough so that (at least) two of

α, β, and δ become tangent to each other. This can be done by choosing r to be half the distance between the closest two of the three given circles, this distance being measured from circumference to circumference along the line of centers. Change the original notation if necessary so that the new β is tangent to the new δ at G (Figures 4.46, 4.47, and 4.48).

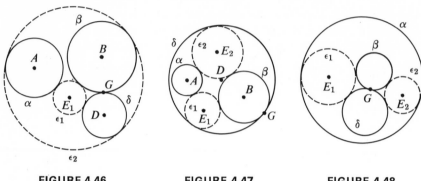

FIGURE 4.46   FIGURE 4.47   FIGURE 4.48

Now invert in any circle γ centered at G. Then β' and δ' become parallel lines while α' remains a circle (primes denote inv γ), as in Figure 4.49.

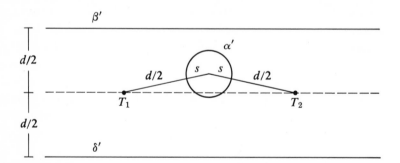

FIGURE 4.49

Exercise. Why must α' be between β' and δ'? (*Hint.* If α' were above β', how many ways would there be for getting from points of δ' to points of α' along circular arcs or line segments?)

Finally, for any circle ε tangent to α, β, and δ as in Figures 4.45, 4.46, or 4.47, ε' will be a circle or line tangent to α', β', and δ'. Since the ε we want clearly doesn't contain G, the ε' we want is a circle. Its radius is half the distance d between β' and δ'. Hence the center of ε' must be one of the two points T_1 and T_2 on the dotted line whose distance from the center S of α' is $(d/2) + s$, s the radius of α'.

These points T_1 and T_2 enable us to draw two "solution circles" ε' which, when inverted in γ, will give us two solution circles for Figure 4.46, 4.47, or 4.48. The centers of these last solution circles will be the points E_1 and E_2 that we wanted in Figures 4.43 and 4.44. ⬚

Problem 5. (a) Describe a ruler and compass construction for a circle which is tangent to a given circle δ and passes through two given distinct points A and B both exterior to the disk bounded by δ. (*Hint.* Invert in a circle centered at A.)

(b) Carry out the construction for some particular selection of A, B, and δ.

The following problem will provide a review of a great deal of the material covered in this chapter.

Problem 6*. Starting with some particular non-intersecting circles α, β, and δ of unequal radii, construct a circle tangent to them. (In order for the construction to be readable, each part should be done in a separate diagram, and several colors should be used.)

Problem 7. (a) Let $\beta = \text{circle}(B, b)$ be inside $\delta = \text{circle}(D, d)$ as in Figure 4.50. Show that the locus of the center E of a circle ε tangent to β externally and δ internally is an ellipse. (*Hint.* Coordinate geometry is hopelessly messy. Try the "sum of the distances" definition of an ellipse.)

(b) Describe a ruler, compass, and ellipse-string solution for the case of the problem of Apollonius shown in Figure 4.44. (This will be much simpler than the construction in the text. An *ellipse-string* is a string fastened to the page at two points A and B and of length $> \text{dist}(A, B)$, as in Figure 4.51. A pencil point P then draws an ellipse (dotted in the figure) by moving in such a way that it always pulls the string taut.)

(c) Carry out (b) for some particular choice of α, β, and δ.

Problem 8. What happens to the locus of point E in Problem 7(a) when neither β nor δ is inside the other? when β is a line and δ a circle which does not intersect β?

There are two applications of inversion which don't fit in with the present exposition, but which are too impressive to be ignored. The first is

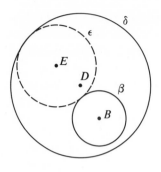

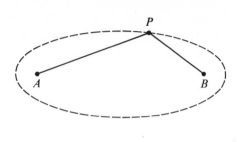

FIGURE 4.50   FIGURE 4.51

Feuerbach's theorem that the nine-point circle of a triangle is tangent to the inscribed circle and all three of the exscribed (e-scribed) circles.*

The other application is a second approach to the problem which suggested Peaucellier's cell—the fact that a straight-edge copies rather than draws line segments. The theorem states that any construction which can be carried out with straight-edge and compass can, in fact, be carried out with compass alone (provided one is content to never actually see a line segment). For example, if λ is the line determined by given points A and B, and μ the line determined by C and D, then the point P where λ meets μ can be found with compass alone. Again, given three distinct points A, X, B it is possible to construct with compass alone, a point Y such that line XY bisects angle AXB. This theorem (one of whose proofs uses inversion) has been omitted because of the complications and subtleties involved in saying exactly what "any construction" means.†

We conclude with some problems.

ANGLES BETWEEN CIRCLES

Problem 9. Show that the number of circles or lines perpendicular to

---

* The interested reader can find the details in *College Geometry* by N. Altshiller-Court (Johnson Publ. Co., U.S.A., 1925), p. 213, or in *Geometry* by H. Eves (Allyn and Bacon, Boston, 1963), p. 159.
† The interested reader can find most of the details and a fairly elementary exposition in *Introduction to Geometrical Transformations* by E. H. Barry (Prindle, Weber, and Schmidt, Boston, 1966), p. 30.

three given distinct circles must be 0, 1, or ∞. (*Hint.* There will be many cases to consider. One possible case-division: (1) At least two of α, β, δ (say, α and β) are concentric; (2) At least two of α, β, δ miss each other but are *not* concentric; (3) At least two of α, β, and δ meet twice; (4) α, β, and δ are all tangent to each other.) Conclude that three given circles can almost always be inverted into themselves.

Problem 10. To show the role played by "non-intersecting" in 4.3.3 and 4.3.4, let β and δ be circles which intersect at exactly two points G and K. Show that no circle $\varepsilon \perp$ both β and δ meets line BD; nor does ε meet any other circle ρ which is $\perp$ both β and δ. ($B =$ center β, $D =$ center δ.)

Problem 11*. Prove the following extension of Theorem 4.3.4 which omits the awkward "non-concentric" hypothesis: For any two non-intersecting inversive circles β and δ there are points G and K in the inversive plane (G separated by β from δ, K separated by δ from β) such that

$$\begin{Bmatrix} \text{the collection} \\ \text{all inversive circles} \\ \perp \text{ both } \beta \text{ and } \delta \end{Bmatrix} = \begin{Bmatrix} \text{the collection} \\ \text{all inversive circles} \\ \text{containing both } G \text{ and } K \end{Bmatrix}$$

(*Note.* Don't bother to reprove that portion of the theorem already contained in 4.3.4. "Inversive circle" and "inversive plane" were defined in Section 4.2.15.)

Problem 12*. (As in Problem 11.) State and prove an "inversive circle" version of 4.3.3.

Problem 13*. Let G and K be the limiting points of two non-intersecting, non-concentric circles β and δ. If two circles ε and ρ through G make equal angles with β, do they also have to make equal angles with δ?

Problem 14**. Let α, β, and δ be given, non-intersecting circles, none of which separates the other two. Does there always exist a circle or line ε which makes specified (undirected) angles of η, θ, and φ with α, β, and δ respectively? (Author—I don't know the answer to this one).

ANOTHER "STEINER PORISM"

Problem 15. State and prove the analogue of Steiner's Porism suggested by Figure 4.52.

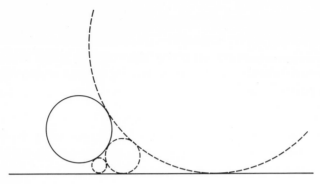

FIGURE 4.52

PTOLEMY'S THEOREM

Problem 16. Prove that *the sum of the products of the opposite sides of an inscribed quadrilateral equals the product of its diagonals.* In Figure 4.53 this becomes

(1) $\text{dist}(A, D) \cdot \text{dist}(B, C) + \text{dist}(A, B) \cdot \text{dist}(C, D)$
$$= \text{dist}(A, C) \cdot \text{dist}(B, D)$$

[Observe that when *ABCD* is a rectangle, Ptolemy's theorem becomes the Pythagorean theorem for right triangles.] (*Hint.* Invert in a circle δ centered at *D*. Then *A*, *B*, and *C* become collinear, so $\text{dist}(A', B') + \text{dist}(B', C') = \text{dist}(A', C')$, primes denoting inv δ. Then use the result of Problem 6, Section 2.)

Problem 17. Let *A*, *B*, *C*, *D* be consecutive vertices of a quadrilateral which *cannot* be inscribed in a circle. Show the "equal" sign in (1) of Problem 16 is replaced by $>$. (*Hint.* Modify the proof of Problem 16.)

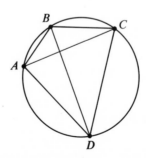

FIGURE 4.53

TWO MORE CONSTRUCTIONS

The following two problems are special cases of the problem of Apollonius. However they have simpler solutions than the general problem because of the extra points of tangency.

Problem 18. Let $\beta = \text{circle}(B, b)$, $\delta = \text{circle}(D, d)$ and $\varepsilon_0 = \text{circle}(E_0, e_0)$ be given, tangent as indicated in Figure 4.54. Construct, with ruler and compass, the circles ε_1 and ε_2 tangent as indicated. (Take the opportunity to check two particular cases of Pappus's theorem 4.3.9.)

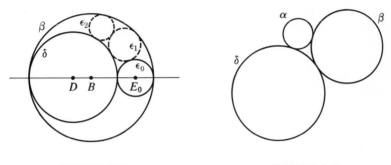

FIGURE 4.54   FIGURE 4.55

Problem 19. Let α, β, and δ be given circles, externally tangent as shown in Figure 4.55. Construct, with ruler and compass, the larger of the two circles tangent to all of α, β, and δ.

4.4   PRESERVING INVERSIVE CIRCLES

We close this section of the book by setting inversion in an abstract context which shows it to be more closely related than one might suspect to isometry and similarity. As in the last section of Chapters 1 and 3, much of this section will be left as problems; and, for the purpose of solving them, the reader should assume that all problems which have occurred earlier in the book are already solved.

Most of this section will take place in the inversive plane, which was defined in Remarks 4.2.15 (in which "inversive circle" and "inversion in a line" were also defined). A function f: (the inversive plane) → (the inversive plane) will be called *inversive circle preserving* (ICP) if:

(ICP) f is $1-1$ and onto, and whenever δ is an inversive circle, so is δ^f.

We have seen that $f = \text{inv } \gamma$ is (ICP). Every isometry or similarity f also becomes (ICP) if we define $\infty^f = \infty$. Also, compositions of (ICP) functions are again (ICP), as are the inverses of these functions. The next question to be raised is now obvious. Its answer is:

4.4.1   THEOREM

Every (ICP) function f is either:
   (i) A similarity, or
   (ii) Uniquely expressible as an inversion in an (ordinary) circle followed by an isometry. (*Notation.* $f = (\text{inv} f) \circ (\text{iso} f)$.)

The proof of this theorem forms Problem 2 below, and will require the following lemma.

4.4.2   LEMMA

Let $\gamma = \text{circle}(G, g)$ and $\delta = \text{circle}(G, d)$ be concentric circles. Then $(\text{inv } \gamma) \circ (\text{inv } \delta) = G(d^2/g^2)$.

Problem 1. Prove the lemma.

Problem 2. Using the following outline (or otherwise) prove 4.4.1.
   (a) If $\infty^f = \infty$, use Theorem 3.3.10 to show f is a similarity.
   (b) If $\infty = G^f$ with $G \neq \infty$, show that for any $\gamma = \text{circle}(G, g)$, the composition $h = (\text{inv } \gamma) \circ f$ is a similarity. Factor h into the composition of a stretch and an isometry. Finally use Problem 1, and conclude that f is the composition of an inversion followed by an isometry.
   (c) Let α and β be concentric circles and h and k isometries such that $(\text{inv } \alpha) \circ h = (\text{inv } \beta) \circ k$. Show that α must equal β, and h must equal k.

(*Hint.* Put both inversions on the same side of the equation.)

One should not be misled by the notation inv f for the inversion part of f. It means inv γ for some $\gamma = \text{circle}(G, g)$ determined by f, and which we will call the *circle of* inv f. What circle is it? The answer will be given in 4.4.5. Observe now that $G^f = G^{(\text{inv} f) \circ (\text{iso} f)} = \infty^{\text{iso} f} = \infty$. Hence:

4.4.3   REMARK

The center of the circle of inv f, for f an (ICP) function $\neq$ a similarity, is $\infty^{f^{-1}}$.

4.4.4   COROLLARY to Theorem 4.4.1

Let f be an (ICP) function. Then for every finite point H such that $H^f \neq \infty$, the following limit exists

$$\lim_{X \to H} \frac{\text{dist}(X^f, H^f)}{\text{dist}(X, H)} = \text{mag}(f, H).$$

It is called the *magnification ratio of f near H*. The notation $\text{mag}(f, H)$ has been chosen to emphasize that the limit depends *only on f and H*, and *not* on the path by which H is approached.

Proof. If f is a similarity, $\text{mag}(f, H)$ is just its magnification ratio, and is the same near all points H.

Let f not be a similarity, and let $\gamma = \text{circle}(G, g)$ be the circle of inv f. Then the desired limit equals

$$\lim_{X \to H} \frac{\text{dist}(X^{(\text{inv} \gamma) \circ (\text{iso} f)}, H^{(\text{inv} \gamma) \circ (\text{iso} f)})}{\text{dist}(X^{\text{inv} \gamma}, H^{\text{inv} \gamma})} \cdot \frac{\text{dist}(X^{\text{inv} \gamma}, H^{\text{inv} \gamma})}{\text{dist}(X, H)}$$

The first fraction after "lim" equals 1 for all X and H (by definition of "isometry"); the second fraction approaches the limit $[g/\text{dist}(G, H)]^2$ by Remark 4.2.16, and this proves the corollary. □

Also, since $\text{dist}(G, H) = g \Leftrightarrow H$ is a point of γ we get:

4.4.5   COROLLARY

Let f be an (ICP) function $\neq$ a similarity. Then the circle of inv f equals the set of points H for which $\text{mag}(f, H) = 1$.

Because of 4.4.5 the circle of inv f is sometimes called the *isometric circle of f.* It is the set of points "near which" f acts approximately like an isometry, namely iso f.

Must an (ICP) function be either direct or opposite? A strictly pedantic answer is "not necessarily" because inversions in circles are neither direct nor opposite. However, we can refine these notions as follows.

DEFINITIONS

An *(ICP)* function f is *conformal* if, for every finite point H such that $H^f \neq \infty$, and for every pair of curves β and δ leading out of H and having tangent rays at H, the curves β^f and δ^f have tangent rays at H^f, and the directed angle from β^f to δ^f at H^f equals the directed angle from β to δ at H. We get the definition of *anti-conformal* by requiring the angle from β^f to δ^f at H^f to be the negative of the directed angle from β to δ at H (for every β and δ).

Since inversion is anti-conformal (Theorem 4.2.11), Theorem 4.4.1 immediately shows:

4.4.6   COROLLARY

Every (ICP) function is either conformal or anti-conformal.
  (i)   A similarity is conformal if and only if it is direct.
  (ii) Inversion is anti-conformal.

Exercise. Let γ be a given inversive circle. Is there an (ICP) function whose square is inv γ?

One of the main steps in the proof of the classification theorem for isometries was the theorem that every isometry is the composition of two or three reflections in lines. No corresponding theorem was proved for similarities. We now fill this gap.

4.4.7   COROLLARY

Every (ICP) function (in particular, every similarity) can be expressed as the composition of 3 or 4 inversions in inversive circles.

Problem 3. Prove Corollary 4.4.7. (*Hint.* Merely combine the theorem, Lemma 4.4.2, the Classification Theorem for Similarities, and the "two or three reflections" theorem for isometries (1.4.7).)

Problem 4. Let $\beta = \text{circle}(B, b)$ and $\delta = \text{circle}(D, d)$ intersect as in Figure 4.56. Show that $(\text{inv } \beta) \circ (\text{inv } \delta) = (\text{inv } \gamma) \circ \text{refl}(UV)$ where γ is the circle centered at $D^{\text{inv}\,\beta}$ and passing through U and V. (*Hint.* Use the following outline.)

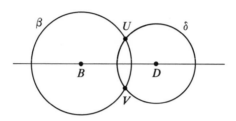

FIGURE 4.56

(i) For some $\gamma = \text{circle}(G, g)$ and some glide reflection r, $(\text{inv } \beta) \circ (\text{inv } \delta) = (\text{inv } \gamma) \circ r$.

(ii) $G = D^{\text{inv}\,\beta}$.

(iii) γ passes through U and V. (Prove the "multiplication theorem" for magnification ratios: $\text{mag}(f, H) = \text{mag}(\text{inv } \beta, H) \times \text{mag}(\text{inv } \delta, H^{\text{inv}\,\beta})$ where $f = (\text{inv } \beta) \circ (\text{inv } \gamma)$.)

(iv) $r = (\text{inv } \gamma) \circ (\text{inv } \beta) \circ (\text{inv } \delta) = \text{refl}(\text{line } UV)$.

We close this section by applying our theory to give a geometric analysis of the *linear fractional transformation*. This is a function of the form (A, B, C, D given complex numbers):

$$Z^f = \frac{AZ + B}{CZ + D} \quad \text{where} \quad \Delta = AD - BC \neq 0.$$

The requirement $\Delta \neq 0$ prevents the numerator from being proportional to the denominator, hence prevents f from being a constant function. However once $\Delta \neq 0$, its actual value is unrelated to the behavior of f, because multiplication of the numerator and denominator by a suitable number can give Δ an arbitrary nonzero value without changing f. It is often convenient to choose the notation so that $\Delta = 1$.

A minor imperfection in the definition of "linear fractional transformation" is that f is not defined for $Z = -D/C$. Instead of eliminating this point from consideration, we take care of this difficulty by extending f to a function: (the inversive plane) → (the inversive plane) via the following definitions:

$$(\text{if } C \neq 0) \quad (-D/C)^f = \infty \text{ and } \infty^f = A/C$$
$$(\text{if } C = 0) \quad \infty^f = \infty.$$

A more uniform way of stating these definitions is

$$(-D/C)^f = \lim_{Z \to (-D/C)} Z^f \quad \text{and} \quad \infty^f = \lim_{Z \to \infty} Z^f.$$

Exercise. Verify that these definitions are indeed equivalent to the original ones.

The classical theorem about linear fractional transformations can be stated, in our terminology, as follows.

4.4.8 THEOREM

Every linear fractional transformation is a conformal, (ICP) function.

Proof. Let f be the given transformation. If $C = 0$, then f is either a translation or a stretch-rotation (by Lemma 3.2.5).

Suppose, now, that $C \neq 0$. Then we can rewrite f in the form

(1)
$$Z^f = \frac{A(Z + D/C) - (AD/C) + B}{C(Z + D/C)}$$
$$= \frac{A}{C} - \frac{AD - BC}{C^2} \cdot \frac{1}{Z + (D/C)}.$$

Thus f is expressed as a composition of (ICP) functions: trans (the origin to D/C), then inversion in circle $(0, 1)$ (by Lemma 4.2.1), then reflection in the real axis (to get rid of the complex conjugate introduced by 4.2.1), then the stretch rotation about 0 determined by $-(AD - BC)/C^2$, and finally trans (the origin to A/C). Hence f is itself an (ICP) function. Since exactly two of the functions in the foregoing composition are anti-conformal, it follows that f is conformal. □

4.4.9   REMARKS

The above proof gave a good way of visualizing f when $C = 0$, namely as a translation or stretch-rotation. But for the case $C \neq 0$, the composition given by (1) is not a very helpful way of visualizing f. For this case we appeal to Theorem 4.4.1: *A linear fractional transformation for which $C \neq 0$ is uniquely expressible as the composition of an inversion followed by a glide reflection* (since f is conformal and inversion is anticonformal, the isometry given by 4.4.1 must be anti-conformal, that is, opposite. The classification theorem for isometries then shows it to be a glide reflection).

     One detail remains to be completed: Find the circle of inversion and the glide reflection in terms of A, B, C, and D. Recall that, for $A = a + bi$ (a, b real) the *imaginary part of A* is the real number $\operatorname{im}(A) = b$.

4.4.10   PROPOSITION

Let f be a linear fractional transformation

$$Z^f = \frac{AZ + B}{CZ + D} \quad \text{where} \quad \varDelta = AD - BC = 1 \quad \text{and} \quad C \neq 0$$

so that $f = (\operatorname{inv} \gamma) \circ r$ for some circle γ and some glide reflection r. Then center $\gamma = -D/C$ and radius $\gamma = 1/|C|$. Also,

     (i) (If $A + D$ is real) r is reflection in the $\perp$ bisector of the line joining the point which goes to ∞ with the point which comes from ∞. (That is, $-D/C$ to A/C.)

     (ii) (If $A + D$ is not real) the line of reflection of r passes through the midpoint $(A - D)/2C$ of the line segment joining $\infty^{f^{-1}}$ to ∞^{f}, and the "glide" of r is $\operatorname{trans}(\overrightarrow{0T})$ where

$$T = \frac{\operatorname{im}(A + D)}{C} i.$$

Proof. Instead of working with f in its given form, rewrite it in the form (1) in the proof of 4.4.8. After substituting $AD - BC = 1$ into (1) we see that the expression can be further simplified by the change of variable (geometrically, change of coordinates)

(2) $$Z = \frac{V}{C} - \frac{D}{C}.$$

In such changes of coordinates it is important to interpret things properly. The letters Z and V in (2) represent *the same point, but are different complex numbers*; namely, if a point P is represented in the old coordinate system by the number Z, and is represented in the new coordinate system by the number V, then Z and V are related by equation (2).

If we denote the old and new coordinates of the point P^f by the numbers Z^f and V^f respectively, then we can rewrite equation (1) in the form

(3) $$\frac{V^f}{C} - \frac{D}{C} = \frac{A}{C} - \frac{1}{C^2} \cdot \frac{C}{V}$$

where the left-hand side of (3) was obtained from the fact that the old and new coordinates of P^f are related by $Z^f = (V^f/C) - (D/C)$ [because of (2)]. Simplifying (3), we get

(4) $$V^f = (A + D) - \frac{1}{V}.$$

In this new coordinate system we easily recognize f to be the composition of inversion in $\gamma = \text{circle}(0, 1)$ and an opposite isometry r: Define the function r by $r = (\text{inv } \gamma) \circ f$, so that $f = (\text{inv } \gamma) \circ r$. Substituting this into Lemma 4.2.1 and (4) we get

(5) $$V^r = V^{(\text{inv } \gamma) \circ f} = (A + D) - \bar{V}$$

Thus r is an opposite isometry (the composition of reflection in the real axis, then reflection in the origin, then a translation) and hence r is a glide reflection.

Before concluding the proof of the proposition (Problem 5 below), we pause to ask, "Where are the new coordinate axes?" To answer this, let X be any complex number. We can draw the *point* X_Z represented by *number* X in the old coordinates, and the point X_V represented by X in the new coordinates. By (2),

$$Z\text{-coordinate of } X_V = \frac{X}{C} - \frac{D}{C}.$$

Therefore the *point* X_V can be obtained by applying, to the point X_Z, the stretch rotation with

center $= 0$
magnification ratio $= 1/|C|$
angle $= -$ polar angle (C)

(this divides X by C) and then applying trans $\overrightarrow{0(-D/C)}$.

Now, to find the new coordinate axes, that is, the set of points X_V

where X is either real or purely imaginary, *merely apply the above stretch rotation and translation to the old coordinate axes* ($=$ the set of points X_Z where X is either real or purely imaginary).

Exercise. For the change of variable

(6) $$Z = \frac{V}{-1 + i} - (2 - i)$$

compute the Z-coordinates of the points 0_V, 1_V, and i_V, and use these to draw the V-coordinate axes. Check your answer with the result stated in italics above. (The angle of rotation will be $225°$, and the new origin will be in quadrant 2. The point 1_V should rotate $+90°$ about 0_V to give i_V.)

Problem 5. Finish the proof of Proposition 4.4.10 as follows.

(a) Starting with equation (5), find two points on the line λ of the glide reflection r. Find the translation part of r by letting V equal a point of λ. (*Answer.* If $A + D$ is *not* real, two distinct points of λ will be $(A + D)/2$ and $(\bar{A} + \bar{D})/2$ and the translation will be trans $\overrightarrow{0M}$, where $M = \text{im}(A + D) \cdot i$. When $A + D$ is real $A + D = \bar{A} + \bar{D}$, so a separate case is necessary.)

(b) Transform the whole answer back to the Z-coordinates, obtaining the statement of the Proposition.

Exercise. For the particular linear fractional transformation

$$Z^f = \frac{(3i)\, Z + (\tfrac{13}{2} + \tfrac{7}{2}i)}{(1 - i)\, Z + (1 - 3i)} \qquad (Caution.\ \Delta \neq 1)$$

write the change of variables [equation (2)] and the form (5) that f takes after the change of variables. Analyze f in the new coordinate system and then translate the answer back to the original coordinates. (*Hints.* The answer should agree with that given by the Proposition. After you make $\Delta = 1$, the change of variables will be equation (6).)

Problem 6. Show that *every* conformal (ICP) *function can be described by a linear fractional transformation*.

Problem 7. Show that every nonzero translation can be expressed as the composition of four, but no fewer, inversions in *ordinary* circles. (*Hint.* First show that, for any distinct points A and B and any positive number m, $A(m) \circ B(1/m)$ is a nonzero translation.)

Problem 8. Show that the set of complex numbers Z such that $Z = 1/(t + i)$. where t ranges through the real numbers, is a circle. Draw the circle.

Problem 9. Prove that if the "onto" requirement is dropped in the definition of an (ICP) function f, then f turns out to be onto anyway. (*Hint.* Using the modified definition, prove the modification of 4.4.1 obtained by interchanging the words "inversion" and "isometry".)

Problem 10. Show that "3 or 4" cannot be improved to "2 or 3" in Corollary 4.4.7. (*Hint.* Show, by considering what happens to ∞, that a stretch rotation with magnification ratio $\neq 1$ and angle of rotation $\neq 0°$ cannot be the composition of two inversions in inversive circles.)

Problem 11*. Let β and δ be two (ordinary) circles which intersect either twice or not at all. Show that the function $f = (\text{inv } \beta) \circ (\text{inv } \delta)$ has exactly two fixed points which, in the non-intersecting case, are the limiting points of the two circles. (*Hint.* Transform β and δ into concentric circles or intersecting lines.)

Problem 12*. Let β and δ be non-intersecting (ordinary) circles. Show that, when $(\text{inv } \beta) \circ (\text{inv } \delta)$ is factored into the form $(\text{inv } \gamma) \circ r$ (r a glide reflection), then the line of reflection of r is $\perp$ the line of centers BD and the translation part of r is zero. (*Hint.* It may help to extract, from the proof of 4.4.10, that the translation part of r (when $\neq 0$) is never perpendicular to the line joining $\infty^{f^{-1}}$ to ∞^f. Problem 11 may also help.)

Problem 13*. Give an analysis of the *conjugate fractional transformation*

$$Z^f = \frac{A\bar{Z} + B}{C\bar{Z} + D} \quad \text{where} \quad \Delta = AD - BC \neq 0$$

which is analogous to that of the linear fractional transformation given in this section.

SUPPLEMENTARY TOPICS

5 | Polygonal Dissection

One of the fundamental notions in geometry is that of area. Yet, almost everybody thinks of the area of a polygon numerically (as a real number) rather than geometrically. The purpose of this chapter is to prove the following theorem, which allows a purely geometric interpretation of the area of a polygon.

5.1 THEOREM

Let $\mathscr{P}$ and $\mathscr{Q}$ be polygonal regions with equal area. Then $\mathscr{P}$ can be dissected into a finite number of polygonal subregions which can be reassembled to form $\mathscr{Q}$.

In order to properly evaluate the depth of this theorem, note that it is not even obvious for a 3 × 5 rectangle and a $\sqrt{15} \times \sqrt{15}$ square. Also, its three-dimensional analogue (for volumes of polyhedra) is false; there is no way of dissecting a regular tetrahedron (= regular triangular pyramid) into a finite number of sub-polyhedra which can be reassembled to form a cube. The proof of this impossibility is more complicated than Theorem 5.1 above. Interested readers can find it in either of the references given at the end of this chapter.

Before beginning the preliminaries to the proof of Theorem 5.1, we clear up some terminology. Recall that a *polygon* is a finite number of distinct points V_1, V_2,..., V_n (the *vertices*) together with the line segments V_1V_2, V_2V_3,..., $V_{n-1}V_n$, V_nV_1 (the *sides*) which must never meet except at their ends, where exactly two will meet at an angle $\neq 180°$. A region of the plane bounded by a polygon was called a *polygonal region* earlier in this book. In this chapter we shall follow ordinary English usage and shorten this to "polygon". (This should not cause the confusion here that it would have caused in the symmetry sections of Chapter 1.) Thus we shall speak of the area or the interior of, say, a parallelogram, rather than of the area or interior of the region bounded by a parallelogram.

If a polygon (= "polygonal region" here) $\mathscr{P}$ can be dissected into sub-polygons and the pieces reassembled to form a polygon $\mathscr{Q}$, we say that $\mathscr{P}$ *is dissectable to* $\mathscr{Q}$. Note that "dissectable to" is a *symmetric* relation; that is, if $\mathscr{P}$ is dissectable to $\mathscr{Q}$, then $\mathscr{Q}$ is dissectable to $\mathscr{P}$. Another simple property we will need is:

5.2   LEMMA   "Transitivity" of dissection

Suppose that $\mathscr{P}$ is dissectable to $\mathscr{Q}$ and $\mathscr{Q}$ is dissectable to $\mathscr{R}$; then $\mathscr{P}$ is dissectable to $\mathscr{R}$.

Proof. Let two dissections s and d of a polygon $\mathscr{Q}$ be given, as in Figures 5.1 and 5.2. We can form the *composite* disection sd by imagining s and d to be printed on transparent films, and then superimposing one of these films upon the other (Figure 5.3).

Now let $\mathscr{P}$ be a polygon dissectable to $\mathscr{Q}$. When the dissection is performed and the pieces reassembled we get a dissection s of $\mathscr{Q}$. In addition, let d be a dissection of $\mathscr{Q}$ such that the pieces of this dissection can be reassembled to form $\mathscr{R}$. Then the composite sd provides a dissection of $\mathscr{Q}$ which can be reassembled to form either $\mathscr{P}$ or $\mathscr{R}$. Hence $\mathscr{P}$ is dissectable to $\mathscr{R}$.   □

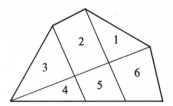

FIGURE 5.1   Dissection s.

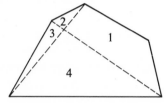

FIGURE 5.2   Dissection d.

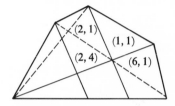

FIGURE 5.3   Dissection sd.

The first step in the dissection process is to cut the given polygon into pieces, each of which will be easy to handle.

5.3   PROPOSITION

Every polygon can be dissected into triangles (whose vertices are all vertices of the original polygon).

Proof.   Let the number of sides of the given polygon $\mathscr{P}$ be n, where $n > 3$. (If $n = 3$ there is nothing to prove.) If $\mathscr{P}$ is a *convex* polygon (that is, all

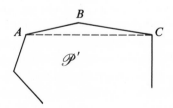

FIGURE 5.4

interior angles $< 180°$), the proposition is a triviality: Let A, B, C be any three consecutive vertices. Then line segment AC dissects $\mathscr{P}$ into a triangle and a polygon $\mathscr{P}'$, with $n - 1$ sides, as in Figure 5.4. If $\mathscr{P}'$ is a triangle we are done. If not we again reduce the number of sides by 1, and repeat this until n has been reduced to 3.

The difficulty in the nonconvex case is due to the fact that it might not be possible to draw a diagonal from an arbitrary vertex A (see Figure 5.5).

To prove the general case of the proposition we show: *In any polygon $\mathscr{P}$ there exists a pair of vertices which can be connected by a line segment lying, except for its endpoints, wholly interior to $\mathscr{P}$.* This lemma will be enough

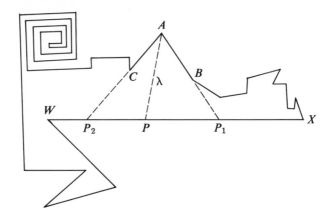

FIGURE 5.5   The nonconvex case

to establish the proposition; for the line segment we find will dissect $\mathscr{P}$ into two polygons $\mathscr{P}'$ and $\mathscr{P}''$, each of which has fewer than n sides. The lemma can then be applied to $\mathscr{P}'$ and to $\mathscr{P}''$, and the process repeated until only triangles remain.

To obtain the lemma, let C, A, B be any three consecutive vertices of $\mathscr{P}$. (Figure 5.5 should help the reader follow the argument.) From A draw a ray λ into the interior of $\mathscr{P}$, and let P be the first point at which this ray meets one of the sides of $\mathscr{P}$. Since $\mathscr{P}$ has only a finite number of sides, each of which can meet λ at most once, there is such a "first point" P.

If P is a vertex of $\mathscr{P}$ we are done. Otherwise P is an interior point of some side WX of $\mathscr{P}$. Now move P toward X, and let P_1 be the first position of P for which the moving line segment AP meets some vertex Y ($\neq A$) of $\mathscr{P}$.

If $Y \neq B$ (for example, if $Y = X$) we are done; and AY is the required diagonal. If $Y = B$ we shift our attention back to the original point P, and move P toward W until the first time the moving segment AP meets a vertex $Z(\neq A)$.

If $Z \neq C$ we are done as before (use AZ); and if $Z = C$, line segment BC will do. □

Exercise. Draw a figure showing a case where Y equals neither B nor X.

5.4   LEMMA

Every triangle is dissectable to a rectangle.

Proof.   Let angle A be the largest angle of the given triangle ABC, so that the altitude AL from L lies inside the triangle. Let (Figure 5.6) line segment PTQ be the perpendicular bisector of AL (P on side AB, Q on side AC of $\triangle ABC$), and then let PR and QS be perpendiculars from P and Q respectively to BC.

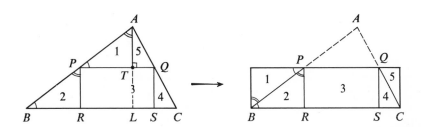

FIGURE 5.6   Triangle to rectangle

Note that $\triangle 1 \cong \triangle 2$. (The triangles are similar by "angle-angle-angle" since $AT \| PR$ and $PT \| BR$; and the ratio of similarity is one because the corresponding sides PR and AT both equal half of altitude AL.) Similarly $\triangle 4 \cong \triangle 5$. Since the sum of angles B and P of right triangle BPR is $90°$, triangles 1 and 5 can be "turned over", as in the right-hand portion of Figure 5.6, to form a rectangle. □

Exercise. How can the above dissection be simplified if $\triangle ABC$ has a $90°$ angle?

5.5   LEMMA

Let $\mathscr{P}$ and $\mathscr{Q}$ be parallelograms with equal area, and suppose that a side of $\mathscr{P}$ has the same length as a side of $\mathscr{Q}$. Then $\mathscr{P}$ is dissectable to $\mathscr{Q}$.

Proof. We can suppose, for the purpose of dissection, that $\mathscr{P}$ and $\mathscr{Q}$ share a common side AB; thus, $\mathscr{P}$ = parallelogram $ABCD$ and $\mathscr{Q}$ = parallelogram $ABXY$. In addition, since the area of a parallelogram equals the product of any side and the altitude to that side, we conclude that

$$\begin{aligned} \text{Altitude to } AB, \text{ of } \mathscr{P} &= (\text{area of } \mathscr{P})/\text{length } AB \\ &= (\text{area of } \mathscr{Q})/\text{length } AB \\ &= \text{altitude to } AB \text{ of } \mathscr{Q}. \end{aligned}$$

Consequently we can place $\mathscr{P}$ and $\mathscr{Q}$ between a pair of parallel lines, as in Figures 5.7 and 5.8.

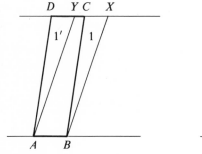

FIGURE 5.7 Overlap on *CD*

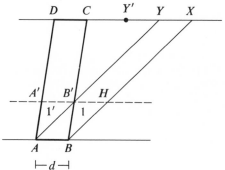

FIGURE 5.8 No overlap on *CD*

Case 1. Line segments CD and XY overlap (perhaps at a single point).

Exercise. Prove that $\triangle ADY \cong \triangle BCX$ and hence complete the proof of Case 1.

Case 2. Line segments CD and XY do not overlap. Then either segment AY meets segment BC at a point B' (as in Figure 5.8), or else BX meets AD; say the former occurs. Draw dotted line $A'B'H$ through B' and parallel to line AB as shown in Figure 5.8. As in Case 1, $\triangle 1' \cong \triangle 1$, and this reduces our task to proving that parallelogram $A'B'CD$ is dissectable to parallelogram $B'HXY$.

Note that length $B'H =$ length $A'B'$ (since $\triangle 1 \cong \triangle 1'$) = length AB. (Length $AA' =$ length BB' since $\triangle 1' \cong \triangle 1$. Thus quadrilateral $ABB'A'$ has a pair of opposite sides equal in length and parallel, and therefore is a parallelogram. Consequently its opposite sides $A'B'$ and AB have equal length.) Hence if we translate parallelogram $B'HXY$ through $d = \text{dist}(A, B)$ units to the left we again have two parallelograms of equal area and which share a side ($A'B'$). As before we apply the procedure of Case 1 or of Case 2, whichever applies, and continue in this fashion.

Will this repetition end after a finite number of steps with the required dissection? Or can it go on forever? To answer this, consider the successive locations $Y', Y'', Y''', \ldots$ of the point Y as it is repeatedly translated d units to the left (Y' is shown in Figure 5.8). Since $\text{dist}(D, C) = d$, some $Y^{(n)}$ must eventually land between D and C. Thus, case 1 applies at the next stage and the dissection is complete. ☐

Exercise. Let q be the quotient and r be the remainder when $\text{dist}(D, Y)$ is divided by d (q an integer ≥ 0) so that $\text{dist}(D, Y) = qd + r$. It is easy to see that, with one exceptional situation, the n of the previous paragraph equals q. What is the exception?

5.6   LEMMA

Every rectangle is dissectable to every other rectangle having the same area.

Proof.   We have to show that any given "x by y" rectangle is dissectable to any "d by e" rectangle whenever $xy = de$. We can choose the notation so that $x \geq y$, $d \geq e$, and $e \geq y$. Note that then $x \geq e$: for if $x < e$, then $xy \leq xx < ee \leq de$ contrary to the hypothesis $xy = de$.

Let $ABCD$ be the given rectangle with length $AB = x$ and length $BC = y$ (Figure 5.9). Since $x \geq e \geq y$ there is a point F on side CD such that $\text{dist}(A, F) = e$. Choose point E on line CD so that $ABEF$ is a parallelogram. The area of this parallelogram is xy; so, by Lemma 5.5 rectangle $ABCD$ is dissectable to parallelogram $ABEF$. (In fact it can be accomplished by Case 1 of that lemma.)

Since the area of parallelogram $ABEF = xy = de$, it follows that the

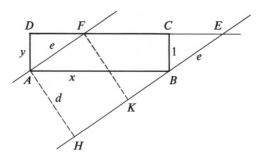

FIGURE 5.9

altitudes *AH* and *FK* of parallelogram *ABFE* have length *d*. Thus this parallelogram has the same area as the *d* by *e* rectangle *AHKF* with which it shares side *AF*. Lemma 5.5 then shows that the parallelogram is dissectable to the rectangle; and then transitivity of dissection shows that rectangle *ABCD* is dissectable to rectangle *AHKF*, completing the proof. □

Proof of Theorem 5.1. Let $\mathscr{P}$ and $\mathscr{Q}$ be given polygons with equal area s^2. It will be sufficient to show that $\mathscr{P}$ is dissectable to an *s* by *s* square $\mathscr{S}$. For then, by similar reasoning, $\mathscr{Q}$ will also be dissectable to $\mathscr{S}$; and so, by symmetry of dissection, $\mathscr{S}$ will be dissectable to $\mathscr{Q}$. Finally, transitivity of dissection will show that $\mathscr{P}$ is dissectable to $\mathscr{Q}$.

To transform $\mathscr{P}$ to an $s \times s$ square, we first dissect $\mathscr{P}$ into triangles (Proposition 5.3), then dissect (and reassemble) each triangle into a rectangle (Lemma 5.4), and then dissect each of these rectangles into a rectangle one of whose sides has length *s* (Lemma 5.6).

Since each of these last rectangles has a side of length *s*, all of them can be assembled into a single rectangle having a side of length *s*. The area of this composite rectangle must be area $\mathscr{P} = s^2$. Thus we have dissected $\mathscr{P}$ and reassembled the pieces to form an $s \times s$ square, completing the proof. □

5.7   REMARKS

Theorem 5.1 can be improved somewhat: The subpolygons which arise in the dissection of $\mathscr{P}$ can be chosen in such a way that, when they are reassembled to form $\mathscr{Q}$, *each side remains parallel to its original position.* This "improved" dissection might, however, require many more subpolygons than the dissection given here.

A proof of this, and of the impossibility of the three-dimensional analogue of Theorem 5.1 are done very elegantly in V. G. Boltyanski's *Equivalent and Equidecomposable Figures.* (This has been translated from the original Russian and printed as a D.C. Heath paperback.)

An interesting selection of dissection curiosities is given in Howard Eves' *Geometry*, Volume 1 (Allyn and Bacon, Boston, 1963), together with a treatment of the three-dimensional case and a somewhat different proof of our Theorem 5.1.

There is also a fantastic theorem of Banach and Tarski which states that if dissection into arbitrary sub*sets* (instead of merely subpolyhedra) is allowed, then a spherical marble can be dissected and re-assembled into a sphere the size of the sun! The proof requires advanced set-theory much beyond the level of this book.

Finally, we remark that although Theorem 5.1 shows that certain dissections are *possible*, the number of pieces required by the proof is often quite large. In particular dissections, shortcuts can often be found which will reduce the work considerably.

Procedural suggestion for the specific dissections in Problems 1–4 below: Draw "before and after" diagrams like Figure 5.6 for the various stages of dissection and reassembly. Then make two copies of the entire dissection, numbering all the subpolygons which arise, and *actually reassemble* one of them.

Problem 1. Dissect a 3 × 5 rectangle and reassemble the pieces to form a $\sqrt{15} \times \sqrt{15}$ square.

Problem 2. Dissect an equilateral triangle and reassemble the pieces to form a square.

Problem 3. Dissect a regular hexagon and reassemble the pieces to form a square.

Problem 4. Dissect the rectangle in Figure 5.10 and reassemble the pieces to form the parallelogram in that figure.

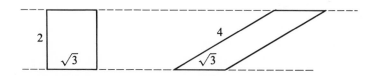

FIGURE 5.10 The dotted lines are parallel

Problem 5.   Prove that the sum of the interior angles of a (not necessarily convex) n-sided polygon is $(n-2) \times 180°$. (*Hint.* Use the "triangulation" proposition, 5.3.)

Problem 6. Show that every polygon has at least 3 angles $< 180°$.

Problem 7. Is it true that for every integer $n > 3$ there is a polygon with *exactly* 3 angles $< 180°$? (If "yes", give a proof; if "no" give an n for which there is none.)

Problem 8. Look up Euclid's proof of the Pythogorean theorem in a copy of Euclid's *Elements*, and note the spirit of dissection in it, which is different from the numerical spirit of most modern proofs.

6 | The Fundamental Theorem of Algebra

This chapter will be devoted to the proof of Gauss's theorem:

6.1   THE FUNDAMENTAL THEOREM OF ALGEBRA

Let $f(Z)$ be a nonconstant polynomial

(1) $f(Z) = A_d Z^d + A_{d-1} Z^{d-1} + \cdots + A_1 Z + A_0$ $(d \geq 1, A_d \neq 0)$

whose coefficients $A_0, A_1, \ldots$ are complex numbers. Then there is a complex number Q such that $f(Q) = 0$.

The number Q is usually called a *root of the equation* $f(Z) = 0$ or a *zero of the polynomial* $f(Z)$. Note that we have switched from exponential notation for functions to ordinary functional notation. When this is done, $f \circ g$ means "first g then f".

The theorem is sometimes stated in different forms. One of the most common is that $f(Z)$ can be factored into d linear factors, d its degree:

$$(2) \qquad f(Z) = A_d(Z - Q_1)(Z - Q_2)...(Z - Q_d).$$

This form is readily derived from the stated one: Since Q is a root of $f(Z)$, $Z - Q$ is a factor of $f(Z)$. Performing the first step of the "long division" $f(Z)/(Z - Q)$ one can show that

$$f(Z) = (Z - Q)(A_d Z^{d-1} + \text{terms of lower degree}).$$

We can now apply the theorem to find a zero of the polynomial $A_d Z^{d-1} + \cdots$ and repeat this procedure until we get (2).

There is one additional form in which the theorem is often stated: that the equation $f(Z) = 0$ has d roots. Strictly speaking, this last statement is wrong, because the equation $(Z - 1)^{13} = 0$ clearly has only one root. The theorem, when stated in this last form, is always an abbreviation for some other longer statement, such as the existence of the factorization (2).

PRELIMINARIES

We will repeatedly use the elementary geometric facts about complex numbers developed in Chapter 2 (often without specific references), especially the following:

$(3) \qquad |A \cdot C| = |A| \cdot |C|$ and, when $A \cdot C \neq 0$,
polar angle $(A \cdot C)$ = polar angle A + polar angle C.

$(4) \qquad |A/C| = |A|/|C|$ when $C \neq 0$; and when A also $\neq 0$,
polar angle (A/C) = polar angle A − polar angle C.

$(5) \qquad \text{dist}(A, C) = |A - C|.$

Euclid's axiom that a straight line is the shortest path between two points implies that $\text{dist}(A, -C) \leq \text{dist}(A, 0) + \text{dist}(0, -C)$. (When does equality hold?) With the help of (5), this can be restated in the form:

$(6) \qquad$ (The *triangle inequality*) $|A + C| \leq |A| + |C|.$

Repeated use of the triangle inequality shows $|A_0 + A_1 Z + A_2 Z^2 + \cdots + A_d Z^d|$ $\leq |A_0| + |A_1 Z| + |A_2 Z^2| + \cdots + |A_d Z^d|$; and then repeated use of (3) shows

$(7) \quad |A_0 + A_1 Z + A_2 Z^2 + \cdots + A_d Z^d|$
$$\leq |A_0| + |A_1| \cdot |Z| + |A_2| \cdot |Z^2| + \cdots + |A_d| \cdot |Z|^d$$

which we will use several times.

Exercise. By a suitable change of variables in (6), show that

(8) $$|U + V| \geq |U| - |V|.$$

DEFINITION

An *open line segment* is a line segment whose endpoints have been deleted. (For example, the set of all real numbers x such that $0 < x < 1$.)

MAIN STEPS OF THE PROOF

The proof of the fundamental theorem will involve many detailed computations. So its proof will be easier to understand if we examine the main ideas first, uncluttered by technical difficulties.

The theorem can be considered a "max-min" problem, namely: Find the minimum value of $|f(Z)|$, where $f(Z)$ is the given polynomial (1).

The first part of the proof will be to show that *no positive number can be the minimum value of $|f(Z)|$*. This will be accomplished by showing:

6.2   PROPOSITION

Let P be any point for which $f(P) \neq 0$, where $f(Z)$ is the given polynomial (1). Then there is an open line segment PV such that, for every point Z of this segment, $|f(Z)| < |f(P)|$.

Note that Proposition 6.2 shows that $|f(Z)|$ can't even have any *relative minimum* $\neq 0$.

Ignoring, temporarily, the details involved in proving Proposition 6.2, which will be contained in Problems 2, 3, and 4, we see that the only possible minimum value for $|f(Z)|$ is zero. Hence all that remains to be shown is: *There is a point Q at which $|f(Z)|$ takes a minimum value*, or, more precisely, such that, for every complex number Z, $|f(Q)| \leq |f(Z)|$.

To see that something really needs to be proved here, note that the function $|1/Z|$ takes all positive numbers for values and has no minimum because it never equals zero. For a slightly less obvious example of this phenomenon:

Problem 1. Define the function $h(Z)$ by $h(Z) = e^x(\cos y + i \sin y)$ where $Z = x + iy$ with x and y real, e is the base of natural logarithms, and $\cos y$ and $\sin y$ are computed by considering y to be a number of degrees. Show that (a) $|h(Z)|$ takes all positive numbers for values (thus no positive number can be the minimum value of $|h(Z)|$), but (b) $|h(Z)|$ never equals zero.

The remainder of the proof consists of strategically subdividing the plane to find a point Q at which $|f(Q)|$ takes a suspected minimum value of $|f(Z)|$; and then showing that, indeed, $|f(Q)| \leq |f(Z)|$ for every Z. This will be done on pages 154–157.

Assuming all the details to be completed, we now have that $f(Q) = 0$, and hence the fundamental theorem is proved.

DETAILS OF PROPOSITION 6.2

We begin with:

Problem 2. Let B_0 be a given complex number $\neq 0$ and c be a given positive integer. Show that there is an open line segment $0T$ at every point W of which (see Figure 6.1)

(9) $$|B_0 - W^c| = |B_0| - |W|^c.$$

(*Hint.* Write B_0 and W in polar form.)

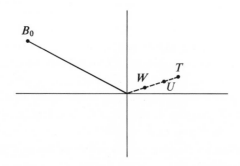

FIGURE 6.1

Problem 3. Let

$$g(W) = B_0 - W^c + B_{c+1} W^{c+1} + B_{c+2} W^{c+2} + \cdots + B_d W^d$$

be a given polynomial in W, for which $B_0 \neq 0$. Show that there is a point U such that

(10) $|g(W)| < |B_0|$ for all points W of open line segment $0U$.

(*Hint.* See Figure 6.1 again. Restrict your attention to points W such that $|W| < 1$. First show that

$$|g(W)| \leq |B_0 - W|^c + |W|^{c+1}(|B_{c+1}| + |B_{c+2}| + \cdots + |B_d|).$$

Then pick U on segment $0T$ of Problem 2, and close enough to 0 to get (10).)

Problem 4. Prove Proposition 6.2. (*Hints.* Let $Z = W + P$ and $g(W) = f(W + P) = A_0 + A_1(W + P) + \cdots + A_d(W + P)^d$. Then, after the parentheses have been "multiplied out" $g(W)$ will take the form $g(W) = B_0 + B_c U^c + B_{c+1} U^{c+1} + \cdots + B_d U^d$ with B_0, B_c, and B_d all nonzero, but possibly $c = d$. Now apply Problem 3.)

6.3   LEMMA

Let $\mathscr{S}_1, \mathscr{S}_2, \ldots, \mathscr{S}_t$ be a finite number of (possibly overlapping) sets of real numbers ≥ 0. Then (at least) one of them, call it $\mathscr{S}'$, has the property:

(11)   For each number r in any of the $\mathscr{S}_j$ there is a number
            s' in $\mathscr{S}'$ such that $s' \leq r$.

Caution. Note that no claim is made that a *single* number s' will work for all r; merely that each time an r is given some s' can be found. Of course, if $\mathscr{S}'$ has a smallest number, that number will do for s' regardless of r.

Proof. Consider first the case $t = 2$. Then there are three possibilities: (i) Some number in $\mathscr{S}_1$ is $\leq$ all numbers in $\mathscr{S}_2$ (then $\mathscr{S}_1$ will do for $\mathscr{S}'$); (ii) Some number in $\mathscr{S}_2$ is $\leq$ all numbers in $\mathscr{S}_1$ (then $\mathscr{S}_2$ will do for $\mathscr{S}'$); and (iii) No number in $\mathscr{S}_1$ or $\mathscr{S}_2$ is $\leq$ all numbers in the other (in which case we can take our choice of $\mathscr{S}_1$ or $\mathscr{S}_2$ for $\mathscr{S}'$).

For the case $t > 2$: First choose an $\mathscr{S}'$, equal to $\mathscr{S}_1$ or $\mathscr{S}_2$, which works for $\mathscr{S}_1$ and $\mathscr{S}_2$. Then choose a new $\mathscr{S}'$, equal to $\mathscr{S}_3$ or the old $\mathscr{S}'$, which works for $\mathscr{S}_3$ and the old $\mathscr{S}'$, and so on. Thus we find an $\mathscr{S}'$ which works for all of $\mathscr{S}_1, ..., \mathscr{S}_t$. $\square$

Note that, although the procedure given above can be carried out any finite number of times, the lemma is false for an infinite number of given sets $\mathscr{S}_j$: merely consider the infinite sequence of sets $\mathscr{S}_1$, $\mathscr{S}_2$, $\mathscr{S}_3, ...$ where $\mathscr{S}_n$ is the set of all positive numbers $\geq 1/n$.

The conclusion of the lemma can be stated in words in a more easily remembered (though slightly less precise) form: *There is one $\mathscr{S}_j$ which has numbers at least as small as do all of the others.*

Notation. Given a set $\mathscr{S}$ of complex numbers, we will use the notation $|f(\mathscr{S})|$ for the set of all real numbers (≥ 0) of the form $|f(S)|$, where S ranges over $\mathscr{S}$.

THE HUNT FOR A MINIMUM

Our object is now to show that there is a complex number Q such that, for every $Z, |f(Q)| \leq |f(Z)|$. The actual value of $|f(Q)|$ will be of no concern to us, since we know that its only possible value is 0.

Let $\mathscr{Q}_1$, $\mathscr{Q}_2$, $\mathscr{Q}_3$, and $\mathscr{Q}_4$ be the four quadrants (Figure 6.2). Then, applying the lemma, we see that one of the four sets of numbers $\mathscr{S}_1 = |f(\mathscr{Q}_1)|, ..., \mathscr{S}_4 = |f(\mathscr{Q}_4)|$ has numbers at least as small as do any of the other three. In order to keep the notation and diagram definite, we will suppose this turns out to be $|f(\mathscr{Q}_1)|$ (analogous reasoning will apply to the

$\mathscr{Q}_2$ $\begin{cases} x \leq 0 \\ y \geq 0 \end{cases}$	$\mathscr{Q}_1$ $\begin{cases} x \geq 0 \\ y \geq 0 \end{cases}$
$\mathscr{Q}_3$ $\begin{cases} x \leq 0 \\ y \leq 0 \end{cases}$	$\mathscr{Q}_4$ $\begin{cases} x \geq 0 \\ y \leq 0 \end{cases}$

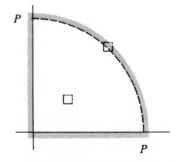

FIGURE 6.2 The quadrants.

FIGURE 6.3 The quarter-disk $\mathscr{D}$: $|Z| < p$, $|Z|$ in quadrant 1; and two squares $\mathscr{U}(m+ni)$

other quadrants). We can restate the conclusion about the $\mathscr{S}_j$:

(12)   For each Z is the plane there is a Q' in the first
             quadrant such that $|f(Q')| \leq |f(Z)|$.

Problem 5. Let p be any number greater than both 1 and

$$\frac{|A_{d-1}| + \cdots + |A_1|}{|A_d|} + \frac{2|A_0|}{|A_d|}$$

Show that $|f(0)| < |f(Z)|$ whenever $|Z| \geq p$. (*Hint.* Consider only values
of $|Z| > 1$ and supply reasons for

$$|f(Z)| \geq |A_d Z^d| - |A_{d-1} Z^{d-1} + \cdots + A_0|$$
$$\geq |A_d| \cdot |Z|^d - |A_{d-1}| \cdot |Z|^{d-1} - |A_{d-2}| \cdot |Z|^{d-2} - \cdots - |A_0|$$
$$\geq |Z|^{d-1} (|A_d| \cdot |Z| - |A_{d-1}| - |A_{d-2}| - \cdots - |A_0|.)$$

Then take Z large enough to make the expression in parentheses
$> |f(0)| = |A_0|.)$

Using the number p of Problem 5 we can draw the quarter-disk $\mathscr{D}$
of Figure 6.3 and then refine statement (12) as follows:

(13)   For each Z in the plane, there is a point $Q_{\mathscr{D}}$ in quarter-
             disk $\mathscr{D}$ of Figure 6.3 such that $|f(Q_{\mathscr{D}})| \leq |f(Z)|$.

(If the Q' of (12) is outside $\mathscr{D}$ let $Q_{\mathscr{D}} = 0$; otherwise let $Q_{\mathscr{D}} = Q'$.)

For each point $m + ni$ in $\mathscr{D}$, where m and n are integers, let $\mathscr{U}(m + ni)$
be the "half-open" square consisting of all points $x + yi$ such that

(definition of $\mathscr{U}(m + ni)$) $\begin{cases} m \leq x < m + 1 \\ n \leq y < n + 1 \end{cases}$

Figure 6.3 shows two such squares.

We continue our "hunt" by observing that these squares partition $\mathscr{D}$
into a finite number of subregions. (In fact, $< (p + 1)^2$ such regions. Note
that some of these squares will also contain points not in $\mathscr{D}$. These "boundary
squares" will introduce a certain amount of inefficiency, but no logical
difficulties.) Hence by applying the lemma to the sets of numbers
$|f(\mathscr{U}(m + ni))|$ we obtain one of them, call it $|f(\mathscr{U}(m_0 + n_0 i))|$, which
contains numbers at least as small as do all of the others; hence at least as

small as can be found anywhere else in $\mathcal{D}$. Hence we can refine (13) to:

(14)   For each Z in the plane, there is a point Q_0 in
$\mathcal{U}^{(0)} = \mathcal{U}(m_0 + n_0 i)$ such that $|f(Q_0)| \le |f(Z)|$.

We can now partition $\mathcal{U}^{(0)}$ into 100 subsquares with sides of length 1/10 and then go through the above reasoning to find a square $\mathcal{U}^{(1)}$ of the form

$$(\text{definition of } \mathcal{U}^{(1)}) \quad \begin{cases} m_0 + \dfrac{m_1}{10} \le x < m_0 + \dfrac{m_1}{10} + \dfrac{1}{10} \\[2mm] n_0 + \dfrac{n_1}{10} \le y < n_0 + \dfrac{n_1}{10} + \dfrac{1}{10} \end{cases}$$

(where each of m_1 and n_1 is one of the digits 0, 1, 2,..., 9) such that

(15)   For each Z in the plane there is a point Q_1 in $\mathcal{U}^{(1)}$
such that $|f(Q_1)| \le |f(Z)|$.

This process of subdivision (the next 100 squares having sides of length 1/100, then 1/1000, etc) can be continued ad infinitum. It is clear that the only point which "survives" the entire elimination process is the number which can be written in decimal form

(16) $Q = (m_0 . m_1 m_2 m_3 ...) + (n_0 . n_1 n_2 n_3 ...) i$.

All that remains to be done now is to show that, for every Z, $|f(Q)| \le |f(Z)|$.

Note that any number, described in decimal notation by $0.0m_2 m_3 m_4 ...$ must be $\le . 1$ with strict inequality in all cases except $m_2 = m_3 = m_4 = \cdots = 9$. It follows, from the definition of $\mathcal{U}^{(2)}$ that either Q belongs to $\mathcal{U}^{(2)}$ or else Q belongs to the dotted part of the boundary of $\mathcal{U}^{(2)}$, that is, its northern or eastern boundary. We can repeat this argument for each $\mathcal{U}^{(k)}$. This observation will be useful in solving:

Problem 6. Let X_k be a point of some $\mathcal{U}^{(k)}$. Show that

$$|f(Q) - f(X_k)| \le p'/(10)^k$$

where

$$p' = \sqrt{2}(p + 2)^d d(|A_d| + |A_{d-1}| + \cdots + |A_1|),$$

p the radius of $\mathcal{D}$. (*Hint.* Write out $f(Q)$ and $f(X_k)$ and subtract. Include an explanation of: $\text{dist}(X_k, Q) \le \sqrt{2}/10^k$ and

$$|X_k^c - Q^c| = |X_k - Q| \cdot |X_k^{c-1} + X_k^{c-2}Q + X_k^{c-3}Q^2 + \cdots + Q^{c-1}|$$
$$\le [\sqrt{2}/(10)^k] \cdot [c(p + 2)^d]).$$

To complete the proof of the theorem, let Z be any complex number. Our "hunt" showed that for each positive integer k there is a point X_k of $\mathscr{U}^{(k)}$ such that $|f(X_k)| \leq |f(Z)|$. Hence, by the triangle inequality,

$$|f(Q)| \leq |f(X_k)| + |f(Q) - f(X_k)|$$

and hence, by Problem 6,

$$|f(Q)| \leq |f(Z)| + \frac{p'}{10^k} \quad \text{(for all } k\text{)}.$$

Since p' is the same for all k, the only way this can happen is to have $|f(Q)| \leq |f(Z)|$, as desired. □

Exercise. What modifications are needed in the proof of the "hunt for a minimum" if "first quadrant" is replaced by "second quadrant" in (12)?

Problem 7. Let $\mathscr{D}$ be an open disk (*open* meaning that the circle which bounds $\mathscr{D}$ is not part of $\mathscr{D}$) and suppose that the nonconstant polynomial $f(Z)$ does not equal zero for any Z in $\mathscr{D}$. Show that there is no point Q of $\mathscr{D}$ such that, for every Z in $\mathscr{D}$, $|f(Q)| \leq |f(Z)|$.

Problem 8. Again let $\mathscr{D}$ be an open disk or open rectangular region and $f(Z)$ any nonconstant polynomial. Show that $|f(Z)|$ has no maximum value as Z ranges over $\mathscr{D}$. (*Hint.* Prove a variant of Proposition 6.2.)

Problem 9. * Let $\mathscr{S}$ be the closed square with vertices at 0, 10, $10i$ and $10 + 10i$ (*closed* means that the boundary of $\mathscr{S}$ belongs to $\mathscr{S}$). Show that there is a point Q in $\mathscr{S}$ such that, for every Z in $\mathscr{S}$, $|f(Q)| \geq |f(Z)|$. (*Hint.* Model the solution after "The Hunt For a Minimum".)

Note that, by Problem 8, the point Q of Problem 9 must be on the boundary of $\mathscr{S}$. This theorem—that a nonconstant polynomial must take a maximum value in every closed rectangle, and that the maximum *must* occur on the boundary of the rectangle—is sometimes called the "maximum modulus theorem" for polynomials (*modulus* is a synonym for "absolute value").

Problem 10. Let $\mathscr{S}$ be a set of real numbers. A *lower bound* for $\mathscr{S}$ is a real number b such that $b \leq$ every number in $\mathscr{S}$. If b is a lower bound for $\mathscr{S}$ and there is no larger lower bound for $\mathscr{S}$, then b is called a *greatest lower bound* for $\mathscr{S}$. Prove that every set of real numbers ≥ 0 has a greatest lower bound. (*Hint.* Build it up in decimal from $m_0 . m_1 m_2 m_3 \ldots$, first m_0, then m_1, etc.)

Problem 11. Use the result of Problem 10 to give a quick proof of Lemma 6.3 of this section.

Problem 12. (a) Prove that every set of real numbers which has at least one lower bound has a greatest lower bound. (*Hint.* Reduce to Problem 10). (b) State the corresponding theorem for upper bounds and explain briefly how to obtain it from (a) of this problem (but do not go into complete detail).

7 | Pythagorean Triples

A discovery of the ancients—perhaps of the inhabitants of ancient, Egypt—was that a right angle can be constructed by pulling a string 12 units long taut at three points separated by 3, 4, and 5 equally-spaced knots (Figures 7.1 and 7.2). This discovery was of great practical value in the construction of walls (of buildings, flood-control devices, etc.) which have to be at right angles to the ground.

DEFINITIONS

A *Pythagorean triple* is a list of three positive integers a, b, c such that $a^2 + b^2 = c^2$. The numbers a and b are called the *legs* and either of them can be listed first; c is called the *hypotenuse* and will always be listed last. Thus 3, 4, 5 and 4, 3, 5 will be considered the *same* Pythagorean triple.

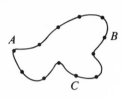

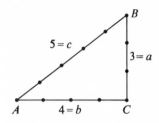

FIGURE 7.1   A string with twelve
equally-spaced knots

FIGURE 7.2   The string pulled taut
A, B, C

The same concept—stated geometrically—is that of a right triangle with *commensurable sides*, that is, sides on all three of which some unit of length can be laid off a whole number of times. (The equivalence of these definitions is an immediate consequence of the Pythagorean theorem for right triangles.)

In addition to the Pythagorean triple 3, 4, 5 which has been mentioned above, other well-known triples are $5, 12, 13$; $8, 15, 17$; $7, 24, 25$. A less familiar one is

(1)
$$a = \quad 3{,}993$$
$$b = 7{,}972{,}024$$
$$c = 7{,}972{,}025.$$

Exercise.   Is there a Pythagorean triple in which $a = 1$?

How can triples such as (1) be found? How many Pythagorean triples are there? This second question has been phrased too crudely; for there are obviously infinitely many, as can be seen by taking arbitrary multiples of 3, 4, 5 (for instance, 6, 8, 10; 30, 40, 50; ...).

To suitably refine the question, recall that a *prime number* is an integer > 1 whose only divisors are itself and 1. (For instance, 2, 3, 7, 11, 29 are primes but 9 and 24 are not.) A list of two or more positive integers a, b, c, ... is *relatively prime* if no integer > 1 divides every number on the list. Thus the Pythagorean triple 3, 4, 5 is relatively prime while 6, 8, 10 is not. (*Caution.* A list of positive integers can be relatively prime despite the fact that no number in it is prime (for example 6, 10, 15, 12).)

Exercise.   Is the Pythagorean triple (1) above relatively prime? (*Hint.* The solution should take ≤ 2 lines.)

The refined version of the question under consideration can now be stated: How many relatively prime Pythagorean triples are there? Since multiplying or dividing the lengths of all three sides of a triangle by a positive real number replaces the triangle by one similar to it, the geometric version of the question is: How many right triangles are there, each of which has commensurable sides, and no two of which are similar?

7.1   THEOREM

Let x and y be positive integers with $x > y$. Then the numbers a, b, c defined by

(2)
$$\begin{aligned} a &= 2xy \\ b &= x^2 - y^2 \\ c &= x^2 + y^2 \end{aligned}$$

form a Pythagorean triple. If, in addition,

(3) x and y are relative prime,
                       and one of them is even

then a, b, c is a relatively prime triple.

Conversely, if a, b, c is any relatively prime Pythagorean triple, then exactly one of a or b must be even—say a is—and there exist numbers x and y such that (2) and (3) hold.

Before proving the theorem we illustrate its content by giving some consequences of it. First, note that by taking $x = 2$ and $y = 1$ we get the triple 3, 4, 5, but in the order 4, 3, 5.

Exercise. Choose some other values of x and y and verify that a, b, and c form a relatively prime Pythagorean triple. Also, answer the question posed immediately above 7.1.

One immediate consequence of the theorem is: *In a relatively prime Pythagorean triple, the hypotenuse is a sum of two squares* (not to be confused with the obvious fact that the *square* of the hypotenuse is a sum of two squares). That this property is not shared by all (non-relatively-prime) Pythagorean triples is shown by the triple 9, 12, 15. Another property of this type is:

7.2   COROLLARY

In every relatively prime Pythagorean triple, the sum of the hypotenuse and one of the legs is a perfect square. [†] The sum of the hypotenuse and the other leg is two times a perfect square.

Exercise. Give a proof. Is this property shared by all Pythagorean triples (not merely the relatively prime ones)?

7.3   COROLLARY

(i) Every odd number $\neq 1$ can appear as the shorter leg of some relatively prime Pythagorean triple.

(ii) There are infinitely many Pythagorean triples in which the hypotenuse differs from the longer leg by 1.

Exercise. Give a proof. (*Hint.* Take $x = y + 1$ in the theorem.)

7.4   COROLLARY

$\sqrt{2}$ is irrational.

Proof.   Suppose that $\sqrt{2}$ were rational, say $\sqrt{2} = m/n$ with m and n positive integers and the fraction m/n in lowest terms (that is, m and n relatively prime), and consider the right triangle whose sides have lengths 1, 1, $\sqrt{2}$ ($= m/n$). Multiplying all three sides of this triangle by n, we get a relatively prime Pythagorean triple n, n, m. Thus, by the theorem, n must be both even and odd!

This absurdity shows that the unproved assumption that $\sqrt{2}$ is rational was wrong, and proves the corollary.   ☐

Another, less roundabout proof will be given in Problem 8.

Exercise. Prove that, for every odd positive integer d, $\sqrt{2d}$ is irrational. (*Hint.* Modify the proof of Corollary 7.4 slightly.)

[†] By a *perfect square* we mean the square of a positive integer.

Problem 1. Prove, by considering the 30°—60°—90° triangle, that $\sqrt{3}$ is irrational.

7.5   PRELIMINARIES to the proof of the theorem

We will need some properties of even and odd numbers.

(i)
$$(\text{even}) + (\text{even}) = (\text{even}) \qquad (\text{even}) \times (\text{even}) = (\text{even})$$
$$(\text{even}) + (\text{odd}) = (\text{odd}) \qquad (\text{even}) \times (\text{odd}) = (\text{even})$$
$$(\text{odd}) + (\text{odd}) = (\text{even}) \qquad (\text{odd}) \times (\text{odd}) = (\text{odd})$$

(ii) Every perfect square is either odd or divisible by 4.

(iii) $(\text{odd})^2 + (\text{odd})^2$ is never a perfect square.

Proof. To prove (ii), note that the square of an even number has the form $(2n)^2 = 4n^2$, while the square of an odd number has the form $(2n + 1)^2 = 4n^2 + 4n + 1 = 2(2n^2 + 2n) + 1 = \text{odd}$.

The proof of (i) is similar, and hence is left as an exercise for the reader. For (iii), note that

$$(2n + 1)^2 + (2m + 1)^2 = 4n^2 + 4n + 1 + 4m^2 + 4m + 1$$
$$= 4(n^2 + n + m^2 + m) + 2$$

which is an even number not divisible by 4 (in fact, it leaves remainder 2 when divided by 4). Hence, by (ii), it cannot be perfect square. □

Another fact we will need to prove Theorem 7.1 is the Fundamental Theorem of Arithmetic: *Every positive integer $n \neq 1$ can be factored in exactly one way into a product of prime numbers in the form*

$$n = p_1^{e(1)} p_2^{e(2)} \dots p_t^{e(t)} \quad \text{with } p_1 < p_2 < \dots < p_t.$$

The power p^e to which any prime p appears in the above factorization is the highest power of p which divides the given integer n. For an example the primes which divide 120 are 2, 3, and 5; the highest power of each of these which divides 120 is 2^3, 3^1, and 5^1; and therefore $120 = 2^3 \times 3 \times 5$. This theorem is proved in most texts on modern algebra or the theory of numbers, and will be omitted here.

It is important to note that the theorem, as stated above, uses the convention that a prime number is to be regarded as the product of a single prime.

7.6   LEMMA

Suppose that the product uv of two relatively prime positive integers u and v is a perfect square. Then u and v must both be perfect squares.

Proof. (Note first that the "relatively prime" hypothesis cannot be omitted: $18 \times 2 = 6^2$ with neither 18 nor 2 a perfect square.)

We first show that *if a perfect square s is factored into a product of primes*

(1) $$s = p_1^{e(1)} p_2^{e(2)} \dots p_t^{e(t)} \quad \text{with } p_1 < p_2 < \dots < p_t$$

then each exponent $e(i)$ must be even. To see that this is true, factor the square root t *of s* into a product of primes, and square this factorization. This will give a prime factorization of $t^2 = s$, and then the "exactly one" assertion of the Fundamental Theorem of Arithmetic will assert that the factorization of s that we get in this way must be the factorization (1). Since the prime factorization (1) of s arises from that of t by doubling all of the exponents, each $e(i)$ must be even.

Now factor the given numbers u and v into products of primes. The "relatively prime" hypothesis shows that no prime which appears in the factorization of u appears in that of v. Multiplying together these factorizations we get a prime factorization of the perfect square uv. By the previous paragraph, all of the exponents in this factorization must be even; but because these are the exponents which appeared in the original factorizations of u and v (since no prime which divides u also divides v), we now see that u and v are perfect squares. ⬚

Proof of the theorem.   We first do the "converse" part of the theorem, that is, we start with a *given* relatively prime Pythagorean triple a, b, c and show that (possibly after interchange of a and b) there exist positive integers x and y such that (1) and (2) below hold.

(1) $$\begin{aligned} a &= 2xy \\ b &= x^2 - y^2 \\ c &= x^2 + y^2 \end{aligned}$$

(2) x and y are relatively prime and one of them is even.

First note that a and b can't both be odd, for it was shown in the preliminaries that $(\text{odd})^2 + (\text{odd})^2$ is never a perfect square. Also, a and b can't both be even, for then a^2 and b^2 will both be divisible by 4, and hence so will $c^2 = a^2 + b^2$. This will force c to be even and contradict the hypothesis that a, b, c is relatively prime.

Thus exactly one of a and b is even. Interchange a and b, if necessary, so that a is even and b is odd. Then $c^2 = a^2 + b^2$ is odd, and hence so is c.

Now consider $a^2 = c^2 - b^2 = (c + b)(c - b)$. Since c and b are both odd, $c + b$ and $c - b$ must both be even, say

(3)
$$\begin{aligned} c + b &= 2u \\ c - b &= 2v \end{aligned} \quad \text{so} \quad \begin{aligned} c &= u + v \\ b &= u - v \\ a &= 2\sqrt{uv} \end{aligned}$$

The surprising fact at this point is that u and v *must be perfect squares*: u and v are relatively prime, for any divisor of both of them would (by (3)) be a divisor of a, b, and c which are relatively prime; hence the lemma can be applied to the perfect square $uv = (a/2)^2$.

Letting $u = x^2$ and $v = y^2$ in (3) we get (1). To get (2) note that any divisor of x and y must divide u and v, hence (by the right-hand half of (3)) must divide the relatively prime numbers a, b, and c. Therefore x and y must be relatively prime. Also, in order for c to be odd, one of x and y must be even and the other odd.

The proof of the theorem is now completed by:

Problem 3. Do the direct part of the theorem (*Hint.* For the "relatively prime" part, it will be sufficient to show that no *prime* number p divides all of a, b, and c. Separate consideration of the cases $p = 2$ and $p \neq 2$ will probably be required.)

The following proposition provides a geometric interpretation of the numbers x and y which appear in the theorem.

7.7   PROPOSITION

Let a, b, c be a relatively prime Pythagorean triple, introduce a rectangular coordinate system as shown in Figure 7.3, and let x and y be as in the theorem. Then (x, y) is the point on the bisector of angle A whose distance from A equals $\sqrt{c}$.

Problem 4. Give a proof. (*Hint.* Use the complex numbers.)

Problem 5. If the sine and the cosine of one of the acute angles of a

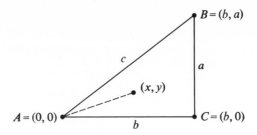

FIGURE 7.3

right triangle are both rational numbers, prove that the sides of the triangle are commensurable.

Problem 6. Is there a set of ≥ 1000 Pythagorean triples a, b_1, c_1; a, b_2, c_2;..., which share of a common leg a?

Problem 7. Can an infinite number of Pythagorean triples share a common leg?

Problem 8. Let x be a positive integer which is not a perfect square. Show that $\sqrt{x}$ is irrational. (*Hint.* Suppose $\sqrt{x} = m/n$ so that $n^2 x = m^2$. Then factor x, m, and n into products of primes and use the Fundamental Theorem of Arithmetic.)

Problem 9*. Find a perfect square such that it, its square, and its square root are all sums of two perfect squares ($\neq 0$).

Index

Numbers in boldface refer to definitions.

Index of Symbols